The Primary Structure of Proteins

MODERN PERSPECTIVES IN BIOLOGY

Under the Editorship of

HARLYN O. HALVORSON *The University of Wisconsin*
MOLECULAR BIOLOGY

HERSCHEL L. ROMAN *University of Washington*
GENETICS

EUGENE BELL *Massachusetts Institute of Technology*
DEVELOPMENTAL BIOLOGY

Published:

A HISTORY OF GENETICS
A. H. Sturtevant CALIFORNIA INSTITUTE OF TECHNOLOGY

MOLECULAR ORGANIZATION AND BIOLOGICAL FUNCTION
John M. Allen, Editor THE UNIVERSITY OF MICHIGAN

BIOSYNTHESIS OF SMALL MOLECULES
Georges N. Cohen CENTRE NATIONAL DE LA RECHERCHE SCIENTIFIQUE,
  GIF-SUR-YVETTE, FRANCE

THE GENETIC CODE: The Molecular Basis for Genetic Expression
Carl R. Woese UNIVERSITY OF ILLINOIS

THE PRIMARY STRUCTURE OF PROTEINS: Principles and Practices
  for the Determination of Amino Acid Sequence
Walter A. Schroeder CALIFORNIA INSTITUTE OF TECHNOLOGY

Walter A. Schroeder

California Institute of Technology

THE PRIMARY STRUCTURE OF PROTEINS

Principles and Practices for the Determination of Amino Acid Sequence

HARPER & ROW, PUBLISHERS · NEW YORK, EVANSTON, AND LONDON

THE PRIMARY STRUCTURE OF PROTEINS:
Principles and Practices for the Determination
of Amino Acid Sequence
Copyright © 1968 by Walter A. Schroeder

Library of Congress Catalog Card Number: 68-11916

To LASZLO ZECHMEISTER
My mentor in chromatography
and to ROBERT B. COREY

CONTENTS

PREFACE

After Sanger and his collaborators had shown that the primary structure—the amino acid sequence—of a protein could be determined, others were quick to apply the methods to other proteins. Almost concurrently, Moore and Stein were developing the analytical methods that have done so much to accelerate the pace of sequence determination. As a result, a vast literature on the subject of sequence determination has grown up, and many results have been forthcoming. Although this information is well known to the active worker in the field, no text covers the subject in detail for the senior undergraduate or the graduate student.

In this book I have tried to write for the student who has a knowledge of organic chemistry, who may have learned something about proteins in a biochemistry course, but who does not know how the structural information about proteins was obtained or who may want to try his hand at a sequence determination. The protein, its isolation, and characterization are considered before the discussion launches into the description of the means by which the primary structure is determined. The discussion is based on currently useful or potentially useful procedures and is not an encyclopedic review of methods that may have been used or proposed. The text evaluates the various methods and indicates what information can be drawn from their application. Experimental details are not given extensively, but may be found in the references. Some historical background is provided. The emphasis has been placed on the chemical means for determining sequences, and the most complete results to date have been cataloged. I have not mentioned, except in passing, the implications of the data in enzymology, biochemistry, biology, and related fields. This would have been tangent to the main purpose. The instructor may do this to the extent that he desires and may supplement the discussion by information that appeared subsequent to the completion of the text.

Another writer, because of his background, interests, and experience, would approach this subject in a different way. My experience has led me to stress column chromatography. The devotees of paper chromatography would emphasize that, but I believe that column chromatography is the more powerful of the two. The reader should not take it amiss that many examples are drawn from hemoglobin, a protein that has engaged my attention for a long time. The fact is that more is probably known about it than any other protein, and it, therefore, serves as an excellent example.

I am grateful for the advice, criticism, and recommendations from Dr. Bernadine Brimhall, Dr. Gary R. Craven, Dr. Hans-Georg Heidrich, Dr. Richard T. Jones, Dr. D. A. Rigas, Mr. J. Roger Shelton, and Professor Laszlo Zechmeister. Each of these has read the manuscript at one or another stage and offered suggestions to me. I especially appreciate the superb typewriting by Miss Allison Kimball who had to overcome the handicap of my handwriting. I want to thank my wife, Ruth, for proofreading with me what was almost a foreign language to her.

WALTER A. SCHROEDER

Pasadena, California
November, 1967

1

INTRODUCTION

Of what value is a knowledge of the amino acid sequence of a protein? Let us answer this question by considering the results of an investigation of ribonuclease, an enzyme which functions by splitting certain specific bonds in ribonucleic acid. When ribonuclease is treated with iodoacetic acid at pH 5.5, an essentially inactive product is formed (Crestfield, Stein, and Moore, 1963 and 1963a). Two reaction products may be isolated: one is totally inactive enzymatically and the other has about 7 percent of the activity of ribonuclease. Further investigation permitted the following conclusions to be drawn:

(1) In each product, a single amino acid residue[1] had reacted.
(2) In each product, the same type of amino acid residue had reacted but in different ways and in different parts of the polypeptide chain.
(3) These residues were separated by 106 residues along the chain.
(4) The two products were formed in a constant ratio of 8:1.
(5) If one site had reacted in a molecule, the other would not.
(6) The two reactive residues are important in producing the enzymatic activity of ribonuclease.

Most of these conclusions could not have been reached if the amino acid sequence of ribonuclease, shown in Fig. 1, had not previously been determined. Because it was known, it could be deduced that the reaction had occurred in the imidazole rings of the histidyl residues at positions 12 and 119.

The example illustrates one reason why many investigators wish to know the amino acid sequence of a protein: they want to be able to correlate the structure with the function, to learn what feature(s) of

---

[1] The reader should refer to Chapter 2 for definitions of unfamiliar words.

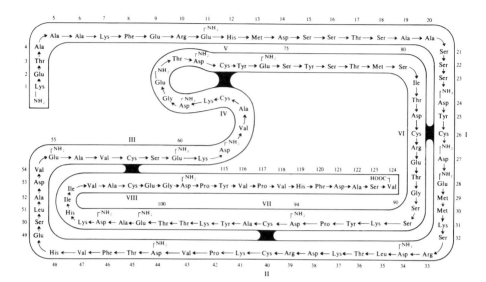

Figure 1. The amino acid sequence of ribonuclease. The abbreviations are defined in Chapter 2 [Source: Smyth, Stein, and Moore, *J. Biol. Chem.*, **238**, 227 (1963).]

the molecule is responsible for its ability to do its job. For this purpose a knowledge of the sequence is vital, but it is only one step toward the goal of understanding the behavior of such a complex molecule as a protein to the same degree that the behavior of a simple organic molecule can usually be understood.

Only in relatively recent years has it been possible to take this first step. Prior to this time, however, it was necessary to dignify a protein by calling it a "molecule" in the accepted meaning of the word through a considerable rethinking of ideas about vague "colloidal" particles, and through a realization of the prominent part that proteins play in all aspects of life processes. Actually, a protein in its native and active state appears to have a well-defined three-dimensional configuration that is determined by the amino acid sequence. One cannot yet predict the three-dimensional configuration from a knowledge of the sequence. However, as more and more sequences are determined and as x-ray investigations unravel the three-dimensional structures, sufficient data may one day be available to permit such a prediction. If this eventuates, the determination of the sequence will be more than the first step toward an understanding of the behavior of the protein.

That proteins are cleaved to produce a mixture of amino acids by hydrolysis in acid or base was known long before the turn of the century, when, in 1902, Emil Fischer and F. Hofmeister independently put forward the idea of the peptide bond and the sequential arrangement of amino acid residues to form the polypeptide chains of a protein. Despite the early enunciation of these ideas, Synge (1943) was forced to state 40 years later that little evidence had been adduced in all those years in their support. This lack of evidence was by no means the result of lack of effort. Fischer himself and many others labored long and diligently to devise methods for the analysis of the mixture of amino acids in a protein hydrolyzate. Fischer's ester distillation method resulted from this effort. The methods required a large sample and were extremely laborious. For example, the Kossel procedure for the determination of the basic amino acids alone required four weeks in the hands of a skilled worker (Vickery, 1946). Despite the difficulties, a few surprisingly good analyses were made and methodology was constantly improved. By the early 1940s, the analyst had at his disposal methods that involved colorimetry, specific precipitants, isotope dilution, and biological assay.[2] Still Synge (1943) in 1943 stated

> To conclude, it seems that the main obstacle to progress in the study of protein structure by methods of organic chemistry is inadequacy of technique rather than any theoretical difficulty. It is likely that new methods of work in this field will lead us to a very much clearer understanding of the proteins.

The prediction proved to be a correct one. Within a few years, radically new methods had been introduced, and their ever-increasing application has produced much information in many related fields. Perhaps more than any other method, the application of chromatography in its varied forms has made possible the development of those methods that Synge believed were necessary. Yet chromatography itself was not new, but also had had its origin at the turn of the century when the idea of the peptide bond and of the polypeptide structure of proteins was first suggested. However, its potentiality was unrecognized for a quarter of a century, and its first reapplication was not related to proteins. It is unthinkable that the knowledge of protein structure that we have today could have become available without the use of the chromatographic method. Because of the sensitivity and selectivity of chromatography, it is possible to complete an amino acid analysis in hours rather than a partial analysis in weeks and to use milligrams (or sometimes micrograms) of material rather than 50 to 100 g. The ability to determine amino acid composition with facility has changed the

---

[2] A good description of the methodology of amino acid analysis in 1945 is to be found in Stein et al. (1946).

direction of research into protein structure and has accelerated the pace at which it is carried out. It would be unfair to infer that this ability has itself brought about this great increase in knowledge. Rather, there has been concommitant advance in methods of isolation, of purification, and of examination and characterization by physical methods. It is these, for example, that tell the investigator whether the object of his proposed study is pure and what its molecular size is.

Despite this progress, the determination of the amino acid sequence of a protein can not be considered a routine matter. Although in Chapter 14 the results of the application of such methods as we propose to discuss will be given, the number of proteins for which a full sequence can be written with reasonable assurance is a mere handful compared to those that have names—let alone those that exist.

It is not intended that the reader of this book will have gained sufficient knowledge of the subject that he can take the book into the laboratory, choose a protein, and determine its sequence. It is not a book of laboratory directions. The ability to do sequence determinations requires an apprenticeship in the laboratory of an experienced worker. Rather the goal of this volume is to convey to the reader an appreciation of the way in which the determination of sequence may be carried out, to acquaint him with some of the chemistry or biochemistry behind the methods, to point out some of the problems that still exist, and to show him what has been achieved. It is not meant to be encyclopedic because the emphasis will be placed on a discussion of methods that have shown good reliability, have produced good results, or have potential usefulness despite limited application. Selected references at the end of each chapter will point to more extensive discussions of the subject either from an historical or a practical point of view.

The two series entitled *Annual Review of Biochemistry* (Annual Reviews, Inc., Palo Alto, Calif.) and *Advances in Protein Chemistry* (Academic Press, New York) are an excellent source of history and methods in protein chemistry as they have developed over the last twenty to thirty years. The topic of the present volume is covered briefly in a review of Canfield and Anfinsen (1963), and specific experimental details for methods in sequence determination are given in a volume entitled *Enzyme Structure* (C. H. W. Hirs, ed., Vol. 11 of *Methods in Enzymology*, Academic Press, New York) and in the book of Bailey (1966). Many other aspects of proteins are described in the compendium *The Proteins: Composition, Structure, and Function* (H. Neurath, ed., 2nd ed., Academic Press, New York).

REFERENCES

BAILEY, J. L. (1966), *Techniques in Protein Chemistry*, 2nd ed., Amsterdam, Elsevier.

CANFIELD, R. E., AND C. B. ANFINSEN (1963), Concepts and Experimental Approaches in the Determination of the Primary Structure of Proteins, in *The Proteins: Composition, Structure, and Function*, 2nd ed., H. Neurath, ed., New York, Academic Press, Vol. I, p. 311.

CRESTFIELD, A. M., W. H. STEIN, AND S. MOORE (1963), Alkylation and Identification of the Histidine Residues at the Active Site of Ribonuclease, *J. Biol. Chem.*, **238**, 2413.

CRESTFIELD, A. M., W. H. STEIN, AND S. MOORE (1963a), Properties and Conformation of the Histidine Residues at the Active Site of Ribonuclease, *J. Biol. Chem.*, **238**, 2421.

STEIN, W. H., ET AL. (1946), Amino Acid Analysis of Proteins, *Ann. N. Y. Acad. Sci.*, **47**, 57–240.

SYNGE, R. L. M. (1943), Partial Hydrolysis Products Derived from Proteins and their Significance for Protein Structure, *Chem. Rev.*, **32**, 135.

VICKERY, H. B. (1946), The Contribution of the Analytical Chemist to Protein Chemistry, *Ann. N. Y. Acad. Sci.*, **47**, 63.

2

ABBREVIATIONS AND CONVENTIONS

As the knowledge about amino acid sequence has increased, abbreviated and conventional representations have been devised to help to present the information in a meaningful way. This chapter presents information that is essential to an understanding of the manner in which data about sequences are described in the literature.

The sequence of amino acids is often referred to as the "primary structure" of the protein.[1]

The names, common abbreviations, and structures of the amino acids that constitute most proteins are presented in Table 1. To avoid confusion in instances in which the abbreviation spells a common English word (met, his), the name of the amino acid will be unabbreviated when it is referred to alone in the text, and abbreviated only when sequences are presented.

Table 1 lists two uncommon amino acids and five derivatives of chemical modification. The other amino acids in Table 1 are usually encountered to a greater or lesser extent in all proteins. In certain instances, for example in small hormones, amino acids of quite different structure may be present.

According to the Fischer–Hofmeister idea of protein structure, a protein may in general be represented by

[1] It is beyond the scope of this volume to discuss the other "structures" of a protein, that is, the so-called "secondary," "tertiary," and "quaternary" structures. The secondary structure refers to the arrangement of the polypeptide chain (see p. 7 for definition) in helical or other regular or irregular manner; the tertiary structure to the arrangement of the secondary structures; and the quaternary structure to the arrangement of subunits.

Reference for Chapter 2, p. 12.

or by

$$\underset{\text{H}}{\text{HN}}\text{—CHR—CO—}\underset{\text{H}}{\text{N}}\text{—CHR}'\text{—CO—}\underset{\text{H}}{\text{N}}\text{—CHR}''\text{—CO—}\underset{\text{H}}{\text{N}}\text{—CHR}'''\text{—CO} \cdots \underset{\text{H}}{\text{N}}\text{—CHR}^n\text{—COOH.}$$

This *polypeptide chain*, as it is called, is comprised of individual *amino acid residues*

$$\text{(or } -\underset{\text{H}}{\text{N}}\text{—CHR—CO—)}$$

because the protein can be considered formally to be put together through the dehydration of two amino acids by the removal of hydrogen from the amino group of one and of the hydroxyl group from the carboxyl group of the other. A polypeptide chain of this type has an amino acid residue at each end that differs from the others. One has a free α-amino group and the other a free α-carboxyl group. This free[2] α-amino group is the *N-terminal end* of the polypeptide chain, and the amino acid residue to which it is attached is the *N-terminal residue*. Likewise, at the other extreme are the *C-terminal end* and the *C-terminal residue*. We must be careful to note that a residue is N-terminal or C-terminal only if an α-amino or α-carboxyl group is involved. Other residues may have a "free" amino or carboxyl group and yet not be N- or C-terminal. Thus, a lysyl[3] residue at any position in the polypeptide chain will ordinarily have a free amino group but it will be an ε-amino group, and an aspartyl[4] or glutamyl[4] residue will usually have a free carboxyl group but it will be a β- or a γ-carboxyl group.

Although substances with many residues in sequence are generally designated as proteins, the term "peptide" is applied to compounds that have relatively few amino acid residues in sequence. A prefix denotes the number of residues; a tripeptide has three residues, a decapeptide, ten, etc.

When a sequence of a hundred or more amino acid residues is known, as it now is in numerous instances, it is much too cumbersome and too prodigal of space to write out a structure in a form such as that

[2] The term "free" is used in a special sense to mean that this α-amino group is not linked to another amino acid residue. The α-amino group may, for example, have an acetyl group attached to it and yet be the "free" end of the chain.

[3] Much as with simple groupings of atoms, the suffix -yl replaces the ending of the name of the amino acid when it is referred to as a residue; thus lysine to lysyl, etc.

[4] From aspartic and glutamic acids. These must be distinguished from "asparaginyl" or "glutaminyl," which refer to asparagine or glutamine.

TABLE 1. *Names, Abbreviations, and Structures of the Common Amino Acids in Proteins*

Name	Abbreviation	Structure
Glycine	Gly[a]	$\underset{\underset{NH_2}{\vert}}{HCHCO_2H}$
Alanine	Ala	$\underset{\underset{NH_2}{\vert}}{CH_3CHCO_2H}$
Valine	Val	$\underset{\underset{NH_2}{\vert}}{(CH_3)_2CHCHCO_2H}$
Leucine	Leu	$\underset{\underset{NH_2}{\vert}}{(CH_3)_2CHCH_2CHCO_2H}$
Isoleucine	Ile (Ileu)[b]	$CH_3CH_2CH\underset{\underset{CH_3}{\vert}}{-}\underset{\underset{NH_2}{\vert}}{CHCO_2H}$
Serine	Ser	$\underset{\underset{NH_2}{\vert}}{HOCH_2CHCO_2H}$
Threonine	Thr	$CH_3CH\underset{\underset{OH}{\vert}}{-}\underset{\underset{NH_2}{\vert}}{CHCO_2H}$
Proline	Pro	CH₂—CH₂ / CH₂ CHCO₂H / N–H ring
Hydroxyproline[c]	Hyp	HOCH—CH₂ / CH₂ CHCO₂H / N–H ring
Phenylalanine	Phe	$\underset{\underset{NH_2}{\vert}}{C_6H_5CH_2CHCO_2H}$
Tyrosine	Tyr	$\underset{\underset{NH_2}{\vert}}{p\text{-}HOC_6H_4CH_2CHCO_2H}$
Tryptophan	Trp (Try)[b]	indole ring—$\underset{\underset{NH_2}{\vert}}{CH_2CHCO_2H}$

TABLE 1—(*Continued*)

Name	Abbreviation	Structure
Methionine	Met	$CH_3S(CH_2)_2CHCO_2H$ $\quad\quad\quad\quad\quad\overset{\vert}{NH_2}$
Cysteine	Cys	$HSCH_2CHCO_2H$ $\quad\quad\quad\quad\overset{\vert}{NH_2}$
Cystine	Cys[d] or Cys	$S—CH_2CHCO_2H$ $\quad\quad\quad\quad\overset{\vert}{NH_2}$ $S—CH_2CHCO_2H$ $\quad\quad\quad\quad\overset{\vert}{NH_2}$
Aspartic acid	Asp	$HO_2CCH_2CHCO_2H$ $\quad\quad\quad\quad\quad\overset{\vert}{NH_2}$
Glutamic acid	Glu	$HO_2C(CH_2)_2CHCO_2H$ $\quad\quad\quad\quad\quad\quad\overset{\vert}{NH_2}$
Asparagine	Asn (Asg, AspNH$_2$)[b]	$NH_2COCH_2CHCO_2H$ $\quad\quad\quad\quad\quad\overset{\vert}{NH_2}$
Glutamine	Gln (Glm, GluNH$_2$)[b]	$NH_2CO(CH_2)_2CHCO_2H$ $\quad\quad\quad\quad\quad\quad\overset{\vert}{NH_2}$
Histidine	His	$CH{=}CCH_2CHCO_2H$ $\overset{\vert}{N}\quad\overset{\vert}{NH}\quad\overset{\vert}{NH_2}$ $\quad\quad\diagdown\!\!_{CH}$
Lysine	Lys	$NH_2(CH_2)_4CHCO_2H$ $\quad\quad\quad\quad\quad\quad\overset{\vert}{NH_2}$
Hydroxylysine[c]	Hyl	$NH_2CH_2CH(CH_2)_2CHCO_2H$ $\quad\quad\quad\quad\overset{\vert}{OH}\quad\quad\quad\overset{\vert}{NH_2}$
Arginine	Arg	$\overset{NH}{\diagdown}$ $\quad\quad C—NH(CH_2)_3CHCO_2H$ $\underset{NH_2}{\diagup}\quad\quad\quad\quad\quad\underset{NH_2}{\vert}$
Ornithine[e]	Orn	$NH_2(CH_2)_3CHCO_2H$ $\quad\quad\quad\quad\quad\quad\overset{\vert}{NH_2}$
Cysteic acid[e]	CySO$_3$H	$HO_3SCH_2CHCO_2H$ $\quad\quad\quad\quad\quad\overset{\vert}{NH_2}$

TABLE 1—(*Continued*)

Name	Abbreviation	Structure
Carboxymethylcysteine[e]	CM-cys	$HO_2CCH_2SCH_2CHCO_2H$ $\qquad\qquad\qquad\quad |$ $\qquad\qquad\qquad\quad NH_2$
β-Aminoethylcysteine[e]	AEC	$NH_2(CH_2)_2SCH_2CHCO_2H$ $\qquad\qquad\qquad\qquad\; |$ $\qquad\qquad\qquad\qquad\; NH_2$
Methionine sulfone[e]	MetSO$_2$	$CH_3SO_2(CH_2)_2CHCO_2H$ $\qquad\qquad\qquad\qquad\; |$ $\qquad\qquad\qquad\qquad\; NH_2$

[a] Sometimes the abbreviations are not capitalized.
[b] The abbreviations in parentheses have also been used in the literature.
[c] These amino acids are uncommon in proteins.
[d] Each abbreviation depicts half of this amino acid.
[e] Proteins that have been modified by chemical reaction may have this derivative.

on pp. 6 and 7. Therefore, sequences are represented by an array of abbreviations which takes the following form *when the sequence is known*:

Val-His-Leu-Thr-Pro-Glu-Glu-Lys.

Although a commission of the International Union of Pure and Applied Chemistry (IUPAC) (1966) has given tentative rules for representing peptides, the representation of a sequence in older literature may take on slight variations. Thus, the abbreviations may not be capitalized, the hyphens may be replaced by periods either on (.) or above (·) the line, or both variations may be used. We shall use the IUPAC rules generally.

By convention, the N-terminal residue of the sequence is placed at the left unless the writer is stressing some other feature of the sequence and then the N terminus is usually clearly identified. To remove all doubt about the order, the above sequence is sometimes written as H-Val-His-Leu-Thr-Pro-Glu-Glu-Lys-OH or with arrows that point in the direction of the C terminus as in Fig. 1.

Prefixed letters (thus, L-Val-D-Pro-L-Asp) may be used to specify configuration. The state of ionization may be represented by $^{\oplus}$H-Val-Leu $\cdots$ Lys-O$^{\ominus}$.

Any undetermined part of a sequence is enclosed in parentheses, and the abbreviations are separated by commas. If a sequence is presented as Val-His-Leu-(Thr, Pro, Glu, Glu)-Lys, it conveys the information that the valyl, histidyl, leucyl, and lysyl residues are arranged in

TABLE 2. *Miscellaneous Abbreviations and Information about Groups and Reagents Common in Sequence Determination*

Abbreviation	Name	Structure	Usage described
DNFB FDNB	2,4-dinitro-1-fluorobenzene 1-fluoro-2,4-dinitrobenzene	*(structure: benzene ring with F, NO$_2$, NO$_2$)*	p. 70
DNP—	dinitrophenyl	*(structure: benzene ring with NO$_2$, NO$_2$)*	p. 70
· · ·	phenylisothiocyanate	*(structure: phenyl—N=C=S)*	p. 74
PTC—	phenylthiocarbamyl	*(structure: phenyl—N(H)—C(=S)—)*	p. 74
PTH—[a]	phenylthiohydantoin	*(structure: phenylthiohydantoin ring)*	p. 74
LAP	leucine aminopeptidase	enzyme	p. 145
CBP—A	carboxypeptidase A	enzyme	pp. 84, 145
CBP—B	carboxypeptidase B	enzyme	pp. 84, 145
DNS—Cl	1-dimethylaminonaph- thalene-5-sulfonyl chloride	*(structure: naphthalene with N(CH$_3$)$_2$, SO$_2$, Cl)*	p. 77
DNS—	dansyl	*(structure: naphthalene with N(CH$_3$)$_2$, SO$_2$)*	p. 77

[a] Used in conjunction with the name of an amino acid as PTH-glycine.

the indicated order but that the sequence of the threonyl, prolyl, and the two glutamyl residues is unknown.

Some use has been made of a still more abbreviated system that uses only a single letter to designate each residue. This type of representation is of value for comparison of sequences by computers but has not yet gained wide acceptance.

Numerous other abbreviations are frequently employed to represent groups or reagents that are used in the chemistry of sequence determination. A heterogeneous array of these is given in Table 2.

REFERENCE

IUPAC-IUB Combined Commission on Biochemical Nomenclature (1966), Abbreviations and Symbols for Chemical Names of Special Interest in Biological Chemistry—Revised Tentative Rules (1965), *J. Biol. Chem.*, **241**, 527.

3

COMMONLY USED METHODS

The ability to determine the sequence of a protein derives largely from the "new methods" that were necessary as Synge pointed out in 1943.

Because it is important to understand the principles of the commonly used methods, this chapter will present this basic information. Details of procedure and application to specific problems vary greatly, but these can be supplied in later chapters on the background that this chapter provides.

THE CHROMATOGRAPHIC METHOD

Mention has already been made of the importance of the chromatographic method in the determination of the amino acid sequence of proteins. Chromatography is a procedure for separating mixtures. It is a dynamic method and requires that the fluid phase in which the mixture is dissolved be passed over a stationary phase[1] and that there be a distribution of the substances to be separated between the stationary phase and the fluid phase. The stationary phase may take many forms, and the fluid may be liquid or gaseous. We shall now describe in a general way some of the more common procedures of chromatography[2] to which reference will be made in the succeeding chapters and for which specific conditions will be described from time to time.

[1] This general term is used because many materials may be used for this purpose and, depending upon their nature, may act in different ways to bring about the separation. The stationary phase often is termed the "adsorbent" although "adsorption" may not be the chief force in its action.

[2] Many books on chromatography have been written. Rather than refer to one or more, the reader is directed to the card catalog of his library.

References for Chapter 3, p. 33.   13

Principles

Let us describe what would occur in a successful separation of two colored substances by *column chromatography*. In Fig. 2(a), a long glass

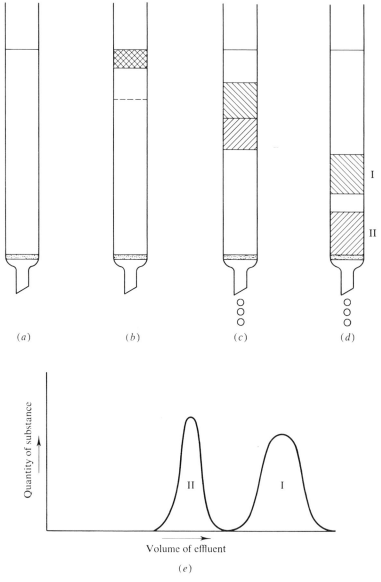

Figure 2. A typical chromatographic separation of two colored substances.

tube with an appropriate closure at the bottom has been packed with some sort of stationary phase. After the solution of the mixture has been placed on and allowed to percolate into the column, the chromatogram will have the appearance of Fig. 2(b) in which the substances to be separated have become fixed in the crosshatched upper portion and the solvent has penetrated to the position of the dashed line. If, now, an appropriate solvent, termed the *developer*, is allowed to percolate through the column and eventually drip from the bottom of the tube, it will cause the components of the mixture to move down the column. Their imminent separation may be apparent as in Fig. 2(c) if the two are of a different color. Eventually, the separation will be complete as in Fig. 2(d), and the chromatogram may be continued until both have been completely washed or *eluted* from the column. If the effluent from the column is collected in small fractions and each fraction is then examined analytically for quantity of substance, the results may be plotted as in Fig. 2(e). Substances I and II are commonly called *zones* when seen on the chromatographic column as represented in Fig. 2(d) and *peaks* (German: Gipfel; French: pic) when the results of a chromatogram are presented as in Fig. 2(e). It should be stressed that colorless compounds may equally well be separated, but that some means of detection other than visual inspection is then required. Fluorescence in ultraviolet light, spectrophotometric examination, or addition of a reagent to the effluent to produce a colored substance are common methods of detecting colorless compounds.

What are the requirements for an effective chromatogram? First of all, it is necessary that the substances to be separated be distributed between the stationary and fluid phases regardless of the mechanism by which this distribution is brought about. This distribution may be represented by the equation

$$K = \frac{Q_S}{Q_F}$$

where K is constant and measures at equilibrium the ratio of the quantity Q_S of the substance that is attached to a unit weight of the stationary phase S and of the quantity Q_F of the substance that is dissolved in a unit volume of the fluid phase F. In a chromatographic procedure, equilibrium may indeed be set up, but the constant flow of fluid past the stationary phase sweeps away the quantity in the fluid phase to a position where it must again come into equilibrium with new stationary phase. Likewise, the quantity on the stationary phase must reach equilibrium again with new fluid which contains no substance.

Let us look at the extremes where K approaches infinity or zero.

As we have defined K, the substance will be entirely attached to the stationary phase as K approaches infinity and none will be in solution. Under these conditions, the substance will be strongly fixed and will not pass down the column with any reasonable amount of developer. On the other hand, as K approaches zero, the substance will be almost entirely in the fluid phase and little will be attached to the stationary phase. The substance will move about as rapidly as the developer. On occasion, it may be possible to arrange the conditions of chromatography in just this way so that a particular substance to be isolated may either be strongly fixed or not at all fixed whereas the other substances in the mixture have the reverse properties. It need not be supposed that, if a substance is strongly fixed with $K \approx \infty$, it is irretrievably lost because a change in the developer may make $K \approx 0$.

In our example of Fig. 2, the values of K for substances I and II may be represented as K_I and K_{II}. If K_I equals K_{II} (whatever the value may be), the substances will not separate under these conditions. This does not mean, however, that the substances cannot be separated. They may perhaps be readily separated if the stationary phase, the developer, or both are altered. Clearly, the greater the difference in K, the better will be the separation of the substances.

We have assumed in this discussion that K is constant for a given substance regardless of the total amount of the substance on the chromatographic column, and that one substance does not influence the K of another. Certainly, these assumptions are not always true, but, in most successful chromatographic separations, they may be considered to be true for all practical purposes.

In practical applications of column chromatography, the ratio of the diameter of the column to the length is usually at least $1:10$ and frequently is $1:100$ or more. For a given volume of stationary phase, separations are usually more effective on long, narrow columns than on short, squat ones. In practice, columns frequently are 1 to 2 cm in diameter and 50 to 150 cm in length.

The interaction of a substance with the stationary phase may occur in several ways:

(1) There may be direct interaction between the substance and the surface of the phase.

(2) The stationary phase may merely hold a second fluid phase so that the distribution really involves a partition between two liquid phases (terms such as "partition chromatography" are sometimes used).

(3) The stationary phase may, in effect, be an insoluble acid, base, or salt, and chromatography may be an ion-exchange process (hence, ion-exchange chromatography).

Ion-Exchange Chromatography

Amino acids, peptides, and proteins contain ionizable groups the state of which depends on the pH because of the dipolar ionic character of these molecules. Thus,

$$\overset{\oplus}{N}H_3CHCO_2H \underset{\substack{\text{Low} \\ \text{pH}}}{\overset{}{\rightleftharpoons}} \overset{\oplus}{N}H_3CHCO_2{\ominus} \underset{}{\overset{\substack{\text{High} \\ \text{pH}}}{\rightleftharpoons}} NH_2CHCO_2{\ominus}.$$
$$\underset{R}{|} \qquad\qquad \underset{R}{|} \qquad\qquad \underset{R}{|}$$

It is not surprising, therefore, that ion-exchange chromatography has played an important role in the investigation of proteins and that ion exchangers have become one of the most valuable stationary phases now available. Ion exchangers may be described as cation exchangers and anion exchangers and each of these in turn as weak and strong. Dowex 50 is an example of a strong cation exchanger. It is formed by the polymerization of styrene (vinylbenzene) in the presence of divinylbenzene, which provides cross links between the chains and, in this way, produces mechanical stability. The porosity of the polymer is a function of the amount of divinylbenzene in the polymerization mixture; the more divinylbenzene the less porous is the final product. The designation of a particular type of Dowex 50 as Dowex 50-X2, therefore, identifies it as a polymer that is nominally crosslinked with 2 percent divinylbenzene. The sulfonation of the crosslinked polymer introduces the actual ionic group (the sulfonic acid group) into the resin and completes the manufacture of the ion-exchange resin. Dowex 1, which contains quaternary ammonium groups, is a strong anion exchanger, whereas weak anion exchangers may have primary or secondary amino groups and weak cation exchangers may have carboxyl groups. Lattices other than polystyrene may be used and, indeed, the available ion exchangers are very diverse. Table 3 lists some of the more commonly used ion exchangers.

Because the ionic form of the amino acid, peptide, or protein will depend upon the pH of the solution, its chromatographic properties on different ion-exchange columns may be expected to vary widely. Because the ionic character of the various amino acids as a function of pH is different, diverse chromatographic properties may also be expected. Although ion exchange plays a major role in this type of chromatography, the nature of the side chain of the amino acid also has a definite effect on the chromatographic behavior. Actually, then, by variation in the type of ion exchanger, in the pH, and in the concentration of ionic species in the developer, an almost infinite variety of conditions of

TABLE 3. *Some Common Ion-Exchange Materials for Chromatographic Purposes*

Trade name or designation	Chemical nature	Remarks
Dowex 50 Amberlite IR Bio-Rad AG 50W	Sulfonated crosslinked polystyrene	Strongly acidic cation exchanger; various sizes and degrees of crosslinkage available
Duolite CS Amberlite IRC-50 Bio-Rex 70	Crosslinked acrylic resin with carboxyl groups	A weak cation exchanger
Dowex 1 Amberlite IRA Bio-Rad AG 1	Crosslinked polystyrene with $N^{\oplus}(CH_3)_3Cl^{\ominus}$ groups	Strongly basic anion exchanger
DEAE-(diethylaminoethyl)-cellulose	Cellulose with $-OC_2H_5N^{\oplus}H(C_2H_5)_2Cl^{\ominus}$	A weak anion exchanger
CM-(carboxymethyl)-cellulose	Cellulose with $-OCH_2COO^{\ominus}Na^{\oplus}$	A weak cation exchanger
Phosphocellulose	Cellulose with $-OPO_3^{\ominus\ominus}Na_2^{\oplus\oplus}$	An intermediate cation exchanger
DEAE-Sephadex CM-Sephadex	Crosslinked dextran with groupings as on the celluloses	

development may be devised in order to achieve the desired separations of amino acids, peptides, and proteins. The separation of the amino acids themselves (which will be discussed in more detail in Chapter 5) is an excellent example of the variation that may be required. On Dowex 50, for example, a buffer of definite pH and ionic concentration readily develops some of the amino acids through the column with satisfactory separations, whereas others require excessive volumes of this particular developer. However, some of the slowly moving amino acids may be expeditiously separated by change to a buffer of higher pH but identical cationic concentration. A third developer is required to complete the chromatogram.

Types of Development

The above example illustrates a procedure that is termed "stepwise elution" (or development). Because each developer is followed by a different kind, an abrupt or "stepwise" change in conditions occurs. The alteration in conditions of development can, however, be made gradually by what is called "gradient elution." One way of forming a gradient in concentration is to add a solution of one concentration to a solution of a second concentration and, at a rate equal to the addition, to withdraw the mixture that is being formed. Figure 3 presents schematically two ways in which gradients may be formed. Figure 3(a) shows a "constant volume" mixer, which initially is filled with solution I. As solution is withdrawn[3] from the mixer, an equal volume of solution II enters. With vigorous stirring a gradient in concentration of the type shown in the graph is formed. The formula for the gradient is

$$2.303 \log_{10} \frac{C_{II} - C_I}{C_{II} - C} = \frac{v}{V}$$

where C_I is the concentration of a given substance in solution I, C_{II} is its concentration in solution II, and C is its concentration in the fluid that emerges from the mixer when quantity v has flowed into a mixer of volume V (Alm et al., 1952). For example, suppose that solution I were $0M$ and solution II were $2M$. After a volume equal to that of the mixer had flowed into and out of it, the emerging gradient would have a concentration equal to $1.3M$ or 65 percent of solution II. It is apparent that little change occurs in the outflowing gradient after a volume equal to about twice that of the mixer has flowed in. Only by replacing solution II with another can the gradient be substantially altered. If solutions I and II are similar in concentration, the gradient will be slight; if they differ much, it will be steep. It is also obvious that, if the size of a chromatographic column is constant, the nature of the gradient will depend on the volume of the mixer: the smaller the mixer, the steeper is the gradient.

---

[3] It is usually easier to withdraw solution from the mixer than to force solution II into it.

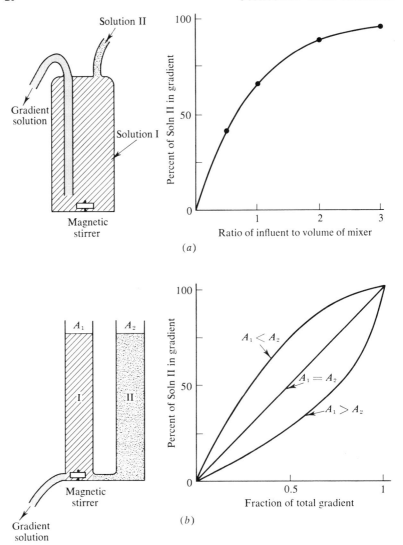

Figure 3. Schematic representation of apparatus for the formation of various types of gradients.

A different and more versatile type of gradient device is described in Fig. 3(b). Two cylindrical vessels of cross-sectional areas A_1 and A_2 contain solutions I and II. As solution is withdrawn, the level of liquid falls in both vessels; solution II passes into solution I, is mixed therewith, and gradient solution is removed. The type of gradient depends on the relation of the cross-sectional areas of the vessels as the graph depicts. The general formula for gradients from this type of apparatus is

$$C = C_{II} - (C_{II} - C_I)(1 - v)^{A_2/A_1}$$

where C is the concentration of substance in the effluent from the mixer, C_I and C_{II} the concentrations of the solutions, v the fraction of the total gradient used, and A_1 and A_2 the respective cross-sectional areas of the vessels (Bock and Ling, 1954). Again, steepness of gradient, etc., is dependent on the several relations already noted above. In contrast to the constant-volume-mixer type of gradient, which can be continued indefinitely, this type of gradient ends when the entire volume has been withdrawn. Another gradient between solutions II and III, for example, must be set up if development is to be continued.

Far more complex gradients than these may be devised (Peterson and Sober, 1959). Regardless of what type is used, it should be obvious that gradients are an attractive means of altering chromatographic conditions.

The first important use of ion-exchange resins in sequence determinations was analytical. Because amino acids are easily and quantitatively determinable in minute amounts by the ninhydrin reaction (Chapter 5), the presence of salts, acids, etc., as components of the developer in concentrations of $0.2M$ or greater was of no consequence. However, if the effluent that contained a given amino acid was evaporated to dryness, the amino acid itself was only a minor contaminant of the buffer components. The procedure, therefore, was difficult to use as a preparative method. The problem was solved in several ways: by conversion to a DNP derivative (Chapter 6), which is no longer dipolarionic and can be extracted from solution; by development with solutions with sublimable salts such as ammonium formate or acetate; or by the exchange of nonvolatile salts for sublimable salts by passage through a second ion-exchange column. The best solution is the use of volatile bases and acids such as pyridine and its substituted derivatives and formic and acetic acids. When these are in the developer, the material in a chromatographic peak may easily be isolated simply by evaporating not only the water but also the volatile base and acid.

Separation by Size

Another type of separation that formally resembles column chromatography is a procedure that depends on molecular size—it is sometimes called "molecular sieving" or "gel filtration." Although columns also are usually used in this process, the stationary phase is composed of porous particles whose pores are of definite and relatively uniform size. Fluid will be present not only in the interstices between particles but also in the pores. A substance so large that it cannot penetrate the pores will be excluded from the particles and relegated to the interstitial volume. In effect, its K will be zero, and it will pass through unretarded. Smaller particles that can enter the pores will have not only the interstitial but also the pore volume available to them. Consequently, they will diffuse into and out of the pores also, and because their effective K is greater than zero, they will separate from the molecules of the larger substance. Although we have used the value of K to describe what is happening in this process, it must be emphasized that, under proper conditions, the separation is brought about mainly by size and partly by shape but not by interaction between stationary phase and substance.

Such molecular sieves are marketed under the trade names of "Sephadex" and "Bio-Gel." Sephadex is crosslinked dextran, and Bio-Gel is polymerized and crosslinked acrylamide. Both types are available in a variety of grades with various "exclusion limits." The exclusion limit identifies the molecular weight of the smallest particle that is excluded from the pore volume. If the exclusion limit is 20,000, for practical purposes molecules of 20,000 and higher molecular weight will pass through the column unretarded. Exclusion limits range from a few hundred to several hundred thousand. Before use, the powdered Sephadex or Bio-Gel must be allowed to swell in an appropriate aqueous medium before a column is prepared. A highly crosslinked material of low exclusion limit may imbibe little more than an equal weight of water, whereas one of high exclusion limit will contain more than 95 percent water. Where substances of appreciably different size must be separated, molecular sieving with these materials may be very successful. A single example of the application of these materials will suffice at this point. Reactions of proteins with small molecules frequently are carried out under denaturing conditions in $8M$ urea. At the end of the reaction, the protein may be freed of urea and small molecules by passage through a column of Sephadex or Bio-Gel.

Gas Chromatography

In the above discussion, a liquid has been the material that flows past the stationary phase. In other experimental arrangements, a nonvolatile liquid may be absorbed on some porous solid support, and the fluid may be a gas. This is "gas-liquid" or usually "gas" chromatography. The general principles are the same as we have outlined above, and the substances to be separated are partitioned between liquid and gas. Such a process can be effective only if the substances in the mixture can be volatilized and carried by the stream of gas. Gas chromatography has had relatively little application to the study of protein structure because of the involatility of amino acids, peptides, and proteins. However, acyl amino acid esters of various kinds have appreciable volatility and have been used in devising analytical schemes for the determination of amino acid composition. We have, therefore, in a sense now come full circle back to an early analytical method for amino acids: Emil Fischer's ester distillation method in 1901 depended for separation on the distillation of the ethyl esters of the neutral amino acids under reduced pressure. The speed with which gas chromatograms may be carried out makes the procedure especially attractive. Complex separations frequently require less than an hour. Gas chromatographic equipment of many types and with many features is available commercially.

Paper Chromatography

The first widespread application of chromatography to problems of protein structure actually took an entirely different form. The method is commonly referred to as "paper chromatography." Its very simplicity has endeared it to many investigators. In practice, a drop or two of liquid that contains the mixture to be separated is placed several centimeters from an edge or corner of a sheet of filter paper and is permitted to dry. If now a solvent is allowed to pass from the edge nearest the spot to the opposite edge, the substances will be carried along as they are on a column and separated from each other if the conditions are correctly chosen. The chromatography of ink is one of the simplest illustrations of the method. This is depicted in Fig. 4. After spots (2- or 3-mm diameter) of different inks have been placed on filter paper as indicated and allowed to dry, the paper is suspended from a watch glass and placed in the beaker so that the lower edge dips into the water. The water will rise by capillary action and separate the pigments of the ink. This is an example of *one-dimensional ascending* paper chromatography. The amount of development is limited by the height to which the developer will rise by capillary action (although this limitation can be circumvented to a degree by special modification of procedure). The paper can also be arranged so that it hangs from a trough that holds the developer. The liquid then descends (*descending chromatography*) and can be allowed to drip from the bottom edge for a long time if necessary. In *two-dimensional* chromatography, the sample

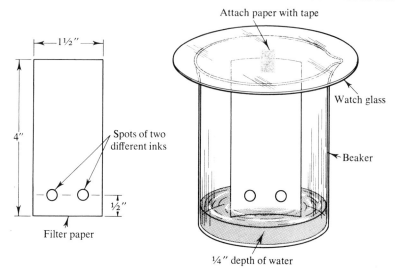

Figure 4. A paper chromatographic separation of the pigments in ink.

is applied near a corner, and development is made in one direction so that the substances are spread along one edge and separated to a greater or less degree. After the chromatogram has been dried, it is developed at 90° to the first direction with another developer. A two-dimensional chromatogram of a mixture of common amino acids is presented in Fig. 5. The number of variations in technique, in apparatus, and in

TABLE 4.   *R_f Values of Selected Amino Acids in a Variety of Solvents*

	R_f		
Amino acid	*Solvent 1[a]*	*Solvent 2[b]*	*Solvent 3[c]*
Arg	0.07	0.46	0.26
Lys	0.07	0.39	0.25
Asp	0.08	0.12	0.34
Glu	0.07	0.24	0.47
Gly	0.12	0.38	0.34
Leu	0.45	0.82	0.84
Phe	0.51	0.89	0.71
Ser	0.16	0.32	0.19

[a] Pyridine 10, isoamyl alcohol 10, water 7, diethylamine 3 by volume.
[b] Phenol, water-saturated.
[c] Ethanol 60, *t*-butanol 20, 88 percent formic acid 5, water 15 by volume.
SOURCE: Schwarz BioResearch, Inc., 1966 Catalog.

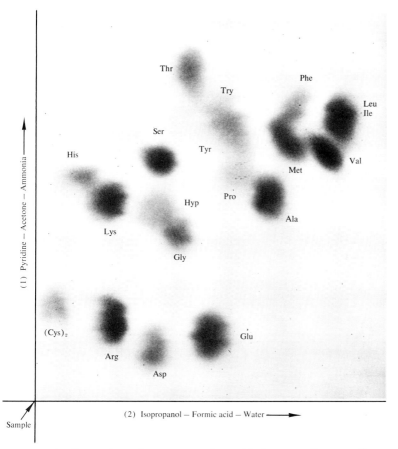

Figure 5. Separation of common amino acids by ascending two-dimensional paper chromatography. After chromatographic development as shown, ninhydrin and isatin were used as color reagents. The colors were stabilized with aqueous nickel sulfate (through the courtesy of Dr. Kenneth N. F. Shaw).

developers for paper chromatography is almost as large as the many investigators who have used the method.

The behavior of substances on paper chromatograms is often expressed and compared in terms of R_f value. The R_f value is the fraction

$$\frac{\text{distance of movement of substance}}{\text{distance of movement of solvent}}$$

It usually relates to the movement of the center of the spot. If R_f is unity, the substance moves as rapidly as the solvent whereas if it is zero, it is fixed. Table 4 lists the R_f values of several amino acids in a selection of solvents. Paper chromatography is frequently used to test homogeneity of amino acids, peptides, or proteins by the application of developers of varied composition; if a single spot is found after several developers have been used, evidence of homogeneity is good. The data in Table 4 show why a variety of developers is necessary: amino acids may not be separated by some solvents but may be widely separated by others. Paper chromatography is of great utility when the quantity of available substance is small, and the handling of large amounts may in fact be burdensome. The method, as applied to the subject that we are considering, may be unsatisfactory if one attempts to remove the substances from the paper because half or more may not be recovered.

"Thin-layer chromatography" has superficial resemblance to paper chromatography. In this procedure, a suspension of some support (for example, a siliceous material) is spread evenly and thinly over a glass plate, and the solvent is evaporated. The support is thus attached to the plate, and samples may be applied and developed much as with paper chromatograms. The procedure appears to have considerable advantage over paper methods. Capacity is good, spots do not diffuse and spread out, and recovery is excellent.

THE ELECTROPHORETIC METHOD

Because amino acids, peptides, and proteins have charged groups the sign and magnitude of which depends on the pH of the solution, we would expect them to migrate in an electric field under appropriate conditions. The fact that they do migrate has been of great use in the study of these molecules. The process is called *electrophoresis*. The rate at which a molecule will migrate in an electric field is dependent upon the magnitude of the charge and the frictional resistance of the molecule to passage through the medium in which it is immersed. The quantitative aspects of the procedure need not concern us here but only the general principles and utility.[4]

So-called *moving-boundary electrophoresis* has been used to a great extent in the examination of the purity of proteins. The principle of this method is illustrated in Fig. 6. Suppose a mixture of substances x and y in a buffer of definite pH were placed in a U-tube and pure buffer were then layered carefully on top to form a sharp boundary in each leg.

----

[4] Electrophoretic procedures have been described in great detail and in specific application (agar gel electrophoresis, disc electrophoresis, etc.). The reader probably can find these volumes in his library.

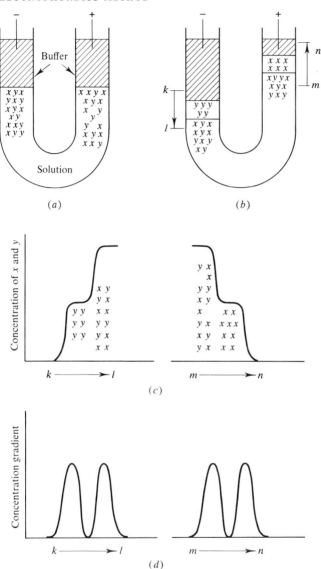

Figure 6. Principles of moving boundary electrophoresis.

If both x and y are negatively charged, they will move toward the anode until after a time the state in Fig. 6(b) will have been reached. Substance x has moved more rapidly than y so that a volume at the leading boundary now contains pure x, a mixture then follows, and finally, near the trailing boundary, pure y is present. If we plot the amount of x and y in the neighborhood of the boundaries $h \rightarrow l$ and $m \rightarrow n$, the graph in Fig. 6(c) results. This information is commonly presented in the form of Fig. 6(d) as a result of the type of optical examination that is usually applied to such boundaries. These peaks actually are the value of the first derivative of protein concentration with respect to position through the boundaries or the concentration gradient as a function of position. Because of the necessary experimental arrangement to maintain boundaries, the U-tube is used. In this description, the left boundary is the *descending* boundary, and the right one is the *ascending* boundary. Certain features should be noted here. A representation as in Fig. 6(d) does *not* indicate complete separation of the two components (as one would expect from a similar presentation of chromatographic data). Only the fastest component at the leading boundary and the slowest component at the trailing boundary will be pure—in between a mixture is found.

Moving-boundary electrophoresis is an excellent analytical procedure but a relatively unsatisfactory one for the isolation of substances. As a result, electrophoresis on solid supports is widely employed both for analytical and preparative work. Just as sheets of paper may be used for chromatography, so they may be applied to electrophoresis. Apparatus may take the form shown in Fig. 7. The sheet of paper S, after having been dipped in a buffer of selected type and pH, is spread upon one of the glass plates P and covered by another glass plate after the sample(s) has been applied in a spot near the center of the paper. The paper drapes over both ends of the glass plate into the electrode vessels V that contain (usually) the same buffer in which the sheet was dipped. To dissipate the heat generated by the passage of electricity during the electrophoresis, especially if high-voltage gradients are used, the glass plates may have to be placed on a cooling plate C through which some refrigerant is passed. A cooling plate on top may even be required. After the current has been passed for the requisite period, charged molecules will have moved in discrete spots in the appropriate direction. If colorless substances have been subjected to electrophoresis, they may usually be made evident by the application of a reagent after the paper has dried. Electrophoresis on paper or sheets of other material such as cellulose acetate or membranes of various types is most frequently used for analytical rather than preparative purposes. Several samples can be placed side by side on the sheet for comparison.

For preparative purposes, the apparatus in Fig. 7 needs relatively little modification. The glass plates and sheet of paper are replaced by a

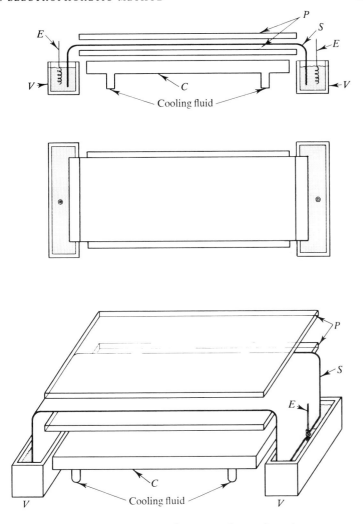

Figure 7. Apparatus for paper electrophoresis.

shallow tray (usually less than 1 cm deep) into which has been poured
some solution or suspension that on solidification forms a porous solid.
For this purpose many materials may be used: starch granules, starch
gel, agar gel, polyacrylamide gel, etc. Electrical contact between block
and buffer in the electrode vessels is made by a wick of cloth or paper.
The sample is usually placed in slots in the block as a solution or
absorbed on paper and placed in the slot. A plastic sheet over the block
prevents evaporation of water during electrophoresis. Although

relatively low current densities reduce the problem of cooling, electrophoresis in a cold room is frequently resorted to. After the electrophoresis is complete, substances may usually be recovered by forming a slurry of support in some solvent and filtering off the solid support. The apparatus in Fig. 7 shows the basic principle of electrophoresis on solid supports, but in practice the variation in design is extreme.

The great advantage of electrophoresis on a support as compared to moving boundary electrophoresis is the separation into discrete components under appropriate conditions much as the zones or spots of a chromatogram.

"Hanging curtain" electrophoresis is a design of apparatus that can be useful for larger scale isolation. A sheet of paper is supported vertically between plates, and an appropriate liquid is permitted to flow continuously from top to bottom. A solution of the substance is also introduced at one point at the top of the sheet. The flow of liquid moves the substances toward the bottom of the sheet, and the potential applied across the width of the sheet moves them to left or right or not at all depending on the charge. The solution of the various substances so separated drops from the lower edge into collecting vessels. In some designs, the sheet of paper is dispensed with and only a film of liquid flows between the plates (carrier free electrophoresis). Because this is a continuous rather than a batchwise procedure, it may be used to separate large quantities of material.

COUNTERCURRENT DISTRIBUTION

Countercurrent distribution (Craig and Craig, 1956) bears a resemblance to chromatography; it, too, is effective because of a distribution between phases—in this case, two liquid phases. If a substance is dissolved in a liquid, if an equal volume of an immiscible liquid is added, and if the whole is shaken vigorously until all is in equilibrium, both solvents will dissolve in each other and the material in each to the extent of their solubilities. Suppose further that an equal amount of solute is in each phase, that is, the distribution coefficient is unity. If the upper phase is now transferred to another vessel, if upper phase is added to the first vessel and fresh lower phase to the second vessel, and if both are vigorously shaken, a new equilibrium will be established in each vessel. If we continue to move the upper phases of each vessel on to fresh lower phase and continue to add fresh upper phase in the first vessel, the solute will move along the train of vessels. But if another solute were also present whose distribution coefficient were greater than

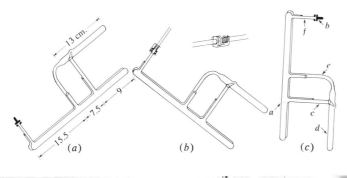

Figure 8. Apparatus for countercurrent distribution. [Source: Craig and Craig, in *Technique of Organic Chemistry*, A. Weissberger, ed., 2nd ed., New York, Interscience, Vol. III, Part I, p. 149 and through the courtesy of Dr. Lyman Craig.]

one (that is, the amount in the upper phase was more than that in the lower phase), it would move along the train more rapidly than the first, and by increasing the number of transfers, the two ultimately would be separated. If the distribution coefficients are very similar, hundreds or thousands of transfers may be necessary to achieve even a partial separation.

The upper portion of Fig. 8 shows the design of a tube for a countercurrent apparatus. A tube of this size may be used with 10 ml of lower phase and an equal or greater volume of upper phase. When a distribution is to be made, all tubes in the apparatus are filled with the appropriate volume of lower phase through part *f*, which is closed to prevent leakage. The sample which may be dissolved in upper phase is added to the first tube of the train. The whole apparatus is then tilted half a dozen times between positions *B* and *A* and allowed to remain in position *B* until the phases separate. The upper phase is transferred through *c* to part *d* when the apparatus is tilted to position *C*. Lower phase remains below level *a* and does not move from tube to tube. When the machine is returned to position *A*, the upper phase passes through *c* into the second tube of the train. Fresh upper phase is then added to the first tube, and the process is repeated. The photograph in Fig. 8 pictures a fully automatic 1000-tube train; the timing and sequence may be adapted to the characteristics of the particular distribution under investigation.

Although countercurrent distribution is a valuable tool, it is less extensively used than chromatography or electrophoresis. Often relatively short chromatographic columns effectively carry out the thousands of transfers that countercurrent distribution requires.

DIALYSIS

Dialysis is commonly used to separate large and small molecules. In its most usual application, the solution of substances to be separated is encased in commercially available cellophane tubing which is securely knotted to hold the solution. The tubing is porous, and when it and the solution are placed in water, those molecules that are smaller than the pores will pass through. Because the membrane may be chosen to retain the protein, it is, therefore, a simple method for removing inorganic ions and small molecules from protein solutions. The same result may be achieved by "molecular sieving" (p. 21 ff).

SPECTROPHOTOMETRY

The absorption of light by a solution is put to good use in protein chemistry for the quantitative determination of substances. It is the method of choice in many instances because it is nondestructive and the determination can be carried out with ease in any of many commercially available spectrophotometers.

The absorption of a compound at any wave length λ in a specific solvent can be expressed in terms of the molar absorptivity (sometimes called molecular or molar extinction coefficient) ε, thus

$$\varepsilon = \frac{1}{cl} \log_{10} \frac{I_0}{I}$$

where I_0 is the intensity of the light incident on and I the light transmitted through a solution of molar concentration c and of thickness l. If ε is independent of concentration, the substance is said to follow Beer's law or the Beer–Lambert law. If the substance follows this law, and if ε has been determined with pure substance, the concentration c of any solution can be calculated if $\log I_0/I$ or the "absorbance"[5] is measured for a known thickness of solution.

In practice, the absorbance is measured at a wavelength at which ε is at a maximum, although this is not a requirement of the method. A common thickness of solution is 1 cm. Likewise, ε is frequently replaced by some other function that relates concentration and absorbance, as for example, mg per 100 ml for a thickness of 1 cm.

REFERENCES

ALM, R. S., R. J. P. WILLIAMS, AND A. TISELIUS (1952), Gradient Elution Analysis. I. A General Treatment, *Acta Chem. Scand.*, **6**, 826.

BOCK, R. M., AND N.-S. LING (1954), Devices for Gradient Elution in Chromatography, *Anal. Chem.*, **26**, 1543.

CRAIG, L. C., AND D. CRAIG (1956), Laboratory Extraction and Counter-current Distribution, in *Technique of Organic Chemistry*, 2nd ed., A. Weissberger, ed., New York, Interscience, Vol. III, Part I, p. 149.

PETERSON, E. A., AND H. A. SOBER (1959), Variable Gradient Device for Chromatography, *Anal. Chem.*, **31**, 857.

[5] Also termed "optical density" in older literature.

4

THE PROTEIN ITSELF

Although great progress has been made in the development and application of methods for the determination of the amino acid sequence of a protein, these methods are not yet so routine that they can be applied with complete assurance of success. Many factors weigh upon the choice of a protein for study and upon the methodology that can be applied. In this chapter we shall discuss some of these factors, indicate what information is desirable before any serious attempt at study is made, and show what value can be derived from preliminary studies. Actually many of these considerations will depend on knowledge that is gained from the application of procedures to be discussed in subsequent chapters.

THE AVAILABILITY OF A PROTEIN

The availability of a protein is a matter of no small moment. Some, such as hemoglobin,[1] are neatly encapsulated, virtually segregated from other proteins, and readily isolable in almost any desired quantity (a half liter of blood from a normal human male contains 65–75 g of hemoglobin). On the other hand, in the same cells with the hemoglobin are many other proteins that individually are only a small fraction of a percent of the hemoglobin and therefore relatively minor contaminants of the hemoglobin. To isolate about a gram of catalase, one of these contaminants, requires 10 to 15 liters of blood. It takes little imagination to appreciate some of the problems that arise if one wishes to study a specific protein from a certain organ of an insect.

[1] The literature source of many comments about hemoglobin may be found in reviews (Schroeder, 1959; Schroeder and Jones, 1965) which in turn contain references to many other review articles.

 References for Chapter 4, pp. 45–46.

One need not think that only those proteins in small percentage are difficult to isolate in pure form. Even if the absolute amount of a protein is high in a given fluid or organ, this protein may be troublesome to isolate in pure form. However, the protein must be pure if its amino acid sequence is to be reliably determined. Let us consider both methods of purifying proteins and of testing their purity.

THE PURIFICATION OF PROTEINS

It is to be expected that a protein has some characteristic by which attention has been attracted to it in the first place. This characteristic can frequently be of use in determining the degree of success of any isolative scheme. Suppose the protein is an enzyme; it would then convert some substrate to a product, and the course of this conversion can presumably be followed in some way. If the course of the purification is achieving its end, the specific activity of the enzyme, that is, the amount of substrate converted by a unit weight of material per unit time, must increase. But even before purification is attempted, the activity can be a useful indicator of the direction that the purification should take. No step that destroys activity can reasonably be included in any initial scheme of purification. If activity is maintained under given conditions, those conditions are of potential usefulness in purification. One can ask such questions as these: is the enzymatic activity altered by heat, by cold, by organic solvents, by high concentrations of salt, by lack of salt, by high pH, by low pH, by adsorption, by dialysis, by enzymes of another type, etc.? If it is stable to heat, perhaps even to boiling in aqueous solution, contaminating proteins may perhaps be precipitated and easily removed. If it is insoluble at a given pH but redissolves with undiminished activity when the pH is altered, the desired enzyme may be precipitated and removed from soluble impurities. If one determines the stability of the enzyme under a variety of conditions, one can with some assurance[2] apply or avoid these conditions in attempts at purification. Enzymes are not, of course, the only proteins to which such considerations apply; any property of a protein— say, the oxygen dissociation curve of a hemoglobin—may be used.

Only the broadest general approaches to purification can be mentioned here. Greater detail may be found in Morris and Morris (1963), Dixon and Webb (1964), and Sober et al. (1965). Consider the simple case of hemoglobin. Although the blood contains many proteins,

[2] The possibility must not be overlooked that a protein may become *less* stable as it is purified. There are many nuances of the problems of protein purification that cannot be elaborated on here.

these for the most part are outside the red blood cell and may be removed by thorough washing of the cells under proper osmotic conditions in 0.9 percent sodium chloride solution to prevent their premature rupture. When the washing is complete, the addition of water ruptures the cells and the solution of hemoglobin may be obtained by centrifuging off the cell debris. It would be incorrect to say, however, that

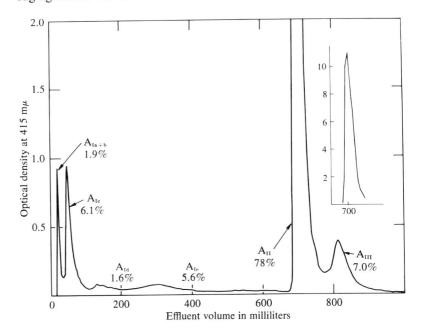

Figure 9. Chromatographic separation of the hemoglobin components of whole adult oxyhemoglobin on a 1 × 35-cm column of Amberlite IRC-50 at approximately neutral pH. The temperature was 5–6°C until 675 ml of effluent when it was raised to 28°C. [Source: Clegg and Schroeder, *J. Am. Chem. Soc.*, **81**, 6065 (1959). Copyright 1959 by the American Chemical Society. Reprinted by permission of the copyright owner.]

the hemoglobin is pure except for the few percent of contaminants as suggested above. Extensive investigation of hemoglobin has shown that the material so isolated from a normal individual contains about 80 percent of one component and smaller percentages of several closely related but definitely distinguishable hemoglobins. This heterogeneity is detectable by electrophoretic and chromatographic means, which may be used to isolate the minor hemoglobin components. A chromatographic separation of the components in the hemoglobin of a normal adult is depicted in Fig. 9.

Suppose, however, that the desired protein is a small percentage of some animal organ and that it is stable to any procedure that we may wish to apply. To release the protein from the cells, the common practice is to comminute the tissue in an aqueous medium, for example, in a Waring blendor. The soluble proteins can then be separated by centrifuging or filtering from insoluble proteins and cell debris. Then may follow a series of precipitations by the addition of an inorganic salt such as ammonium sulfate or of an organic solvent such as ethanol to various concentrations or by change of pH. One procedure may precipitate the desired protein and another the contaminants. By alternation and variation of conditions, the purity of the substance is increased. Often such precipitations are necessary to achieve a reasonable concentration of the protein before resort is had to electrophoresis, chromatography, and related methods. Electrophoresis and chromatography are extremely powerful tools in the purification of proteins and are commonly applied at some stage. In some instances, chromatography alone can be used to isolate a substance from a complex mixture. The isolation of ribonuclease from pancreatic extracts provides an example (Hirs *et al.*, 1953). Figure 10 presents the results of the chromatography of a total pancreatic extract. The ribonuclease so isolated gave good evidence of homogeneity when it was rechromatographed. On the other hand, some preparations of ribonuclease that had been made by conventional methods, which included crystallization, etc., were obviously heterogeneous when examined chromatographically (Fig. 10).

Leucine aminopeptidase (LAP) is an example of a protein whose isolation is far more difficult (Hill *et al.*, 1958). After an acetone-dried powder had been prepared from swine kidneys by ethanol and chloroform precipitation, the powder was extracted with water and two ammonium sulfate precipitations of the desired enzyme were made. Adjustment of pH, addition of magnesium chloride, and heating precipitated inactive material. From the solution, the LAP was then precipitated by acetone at −4 to −5°C. The final purification step required electrophoresis on a starch column in a buffer at pH 8.4–8.6. Even with this extensive purification, the enzyme was not entirely homogeneous.

For many details on the purification of proteins, in particular of enzymes, the book by Dixon and Webb (1964) may be consulted.

As difficult as the isolation of a soluble protein may be, the purification of an insoluble protein is a task that has much greater problems and uncertainties. Structural proteins such as highly crosslinked collagen and the keratins are insoluble. The proteins of membranes, mitochondria, and ribosomes offer further examples. Our knowledge of insoluble proteins correspondingly is limited. An approach to the purification certainly lies in the removal of soluble contaminants, but one can not be certain that an extracting medium penetrates into the

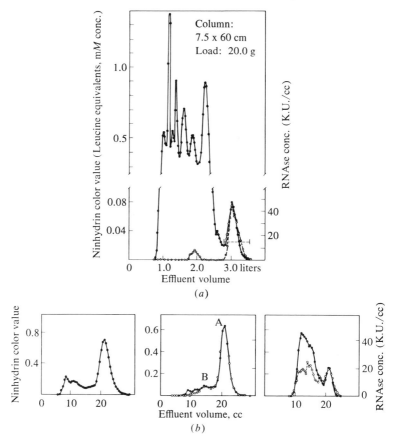

Figure 10. (a) The preparative isolation of ribonuclease from a sulfuric acid extract of beef pancreas on a 7.5 × 60-cm column of Amberlite IRC-50. (b) Analytical examination of several crystalline preparations of ribonuclease on a 0.9 × 30-cm column. ● ninhydrin value; O enzymatic activity. [Adapted from Hirs, Moore, and Stein, *J. Biol. Chem.*, **200**, 493 (1953).]

insoluble particles and removes the soluble substances. Other approaches involve the solubilization of the protein by one or another rather drastic procedure such as the use of strongly acidic or basic media or the actual chemical alteration of the protein. Needless to say, the further fractionation of such a protein and the interpretation of the results from a study of the fractions is fraught with problems because of the possible artifacts or degradations that may have been produced by the procedure.

CRITERIA OF THE HOMOGENEITY OF A PROTEIN

Little thought is required before one comes to the conclusion that the determination of the absolute purity of a protein is a problem of no mean proportions. Basically, the decision in favor of homogeneity lies in the negative evidence of heterogeneity in any test that one may apply. And negative evidence can never be conclusive because a more sensitive test may give positive evidence of heterogeneity. The methods of separation in one form or another are also the basic criteria of homogeneity.

In the discussion above, we have used the activity, in particular the specific activity of an enzyme, as an indicator of progress in purification. When specific activity can no longer be increased[3] by the application of the purification procedure, it does not necessarily mean that the protein is pure. It may simply mean that the limit of the method has been reached and a new one must be applied. If, for example, only precipitation with ammonium sulfate has been used, chromatography or electrophoresis may detect massive impurity.

In the initial stages of purification, the detection of heterogeneity is usually no great problem. It is rather in the final effort to reach the elusive goal of homogeneity that the full array of methodology must be applied. It is then that chromatography and electrophoresis under as many conditions as possible must be used. Purity by these methods must be tested further by ultracentrifugation to determine whether only one type of sedimenting molecule is present. As in other tests, negative evidence of heterogeneity is not positive evidence of homogeneity—a mixture of molecules with identical sedimenting properties may be present. All these methods will have their own special or general means of detecting heterogeneity. The means and the sensitivity of the detection will depend on the method and the protein under investigation. If they are applicable, other techniques such as countercurrent distribution, dialysis, and immunological methods may be used. We can do little more here than to call attention to these means of studying homogeneity. The interpretation of the results of their application to a specific protein may lead to controversy among experts.

---

[3] One cannot overlook the fact that specific activity, in a sense, may decrease during purification if some necessary factor such as a metal is removed. Full and, perhaps, increased activity is then restored when the metal is added.

We must not lose sight of the fact that the determination of the amino acid sequence of a protein is as absolute an indicator of homogeneity as any. The first chemical method that should be applied is the determination of the amino acid composition (see Chapter 5). Constant amino acid composition has no more meaning than constant specific activity, but a changing composition certainly means that this criterion of homegeneity has not yet been met. Because amino acid composition may now be determined with ease, this criterion should be applied more frequently than it has been in the past. Hemoglobin is an excellent example of the way in which increasing sophistication in methods produces positive evidence of heterogeneity. Thus, the first complete amino acid analysis by modern chromatographic methods was made on crystallized adult human hemoglobin that gave little evidence of heterogeneity in electrophoretic or ultracentrifugal experiments. The analysis indicated a single residue of isoleucine in a molecular weight of 66,800 (Schroeder et al., 1950). This result was fortuitous. When chromatography (Fig. 9) separated several hemoglobin components in such a sample, the main component and several minor components were shown to be isoleucine-free. The isoleucine was present mainly in other proteins with little or no heme content (Allen et al., 1958). Another chemical method for assessing purity is the qualitative and quantitative determination of N-terminal residues (see Chapter 2 for definition and Chapter 6 for methods). If the protein shows an integral number of N-terminal residues per molecule, another criterion of homogeneity has been met.

The ability to determine a definite sequence of amino acids in a protein is convincing evidence that it is not merely an array of almost but not quite identical molecules. Although methods of sequence determination do not provide a complete material balance, they are positive criteria that homogeneity has been approached. No better example can be given than to cite the structure of the normal and abnormal human hemoglobins of which there are more than 50 examples of the alteration of a single amino acid residue in 287 (see Chapter 14).

THE MOLECULAR WEIGHT OF THE PROTEIN

As a rough average estimate, each 110 units of molecular weight are equivalent to one amino acid residue. Consequently, we may expect approximately the following number of residues in proteins of the given molecular weights: 55 in 6,000; 135 in 15,000; 550 in 60,000;

4,550 in 500,000; etc. If each of these residues is uniquely situated in the sequence, the complete determination of sequence in a large molecule is a formidable task. However, ever-increasing evidence suggests that, if the molecular weight is of the order of 50,000 or more, there may be identical subunits, which in effect reduce the molecular weight and, hence, the complexity. Hemoglobin provides an example again. With a molecular weight of about 66,000, approximately 600 residues would be anticipated. The molecule actually has four chains in pairs and, therefore, has identical halves. The molecular weight of the minimum unit is about 33,000. Many proteins of nominally high molecular weight have been found to contain identical subunits. Hemoglobin has two identical halves or subunits, fumarase has four (Kanarek *et al.*, 1964), hemerythrin has eight (Klotz and Keresztes-Nagy, 1963), and tobacco mosaic virus has 3,000 (Harris and Knight, 1955)! Further discussion and listing of subunit structures may be found in Sund and Weber (1966) and Klotz (1967). The subunits may be further divided as we have already seen for hemoglobin. In this instance, each half has two different chains of approximately equal lengths (141 and 146 residues). If it can be proved that a protein has identical subunits, the magnitude of the task of sequence determination is measured by the molecular weight of the subunit—a magnitude that may be far less than anticipated. On the other hand, if the protein or the subunit is found to have two or more nonidentical polypeptide chains, another problem arises. Such a protein is basically a mixture of proteins. The determination of the sequence will be much speeded if the different chains can be separated. Consequently, separation procedures must be resorted to: precipitation, electrophoresis, chromatography, countercurrent distribution, and the like. The chains of insulin, which was the first protein whose sequence was determined, were separated initially by Sanger (1949) through precipitation by change of pH. Although the chains of hemoglobin were first separated by chromatography and later by better chromatographic methods, countercurrent distribution, electrophoresis, and precipitation are also applicable.

THE COMPOSITION OF THE PROTEIN

That a protein is composed of amino acids is not the emphasis of this section. Rather, let us consider what a knowledge of the amino acid composition and of possible constituents other than amino acids will tell about potential obstacles in the path of the determination of amino acid sequence. It should be mentioned at this point that procedures for the determination of amino acid composition do not distinguish between the D and L isomers of the amino acids. Whether one or the other or both isomers are present is rarely investigated during sequence studies; it is generally assumed that only L amino acids make up a protein, although D amino acids are constituents of small naturally occurring peptides.

Despite the fact that a protein may be composed solely of amino acid residues, the side chains that distinguish these residues one from the other are by no means identical in their degree or kind of chemical reactivity. Some like those with aliphatic side chains will be generally unreactive, whereas others like the sulfur-containing amino acids will be sensitive to relatively mild outside influences. When the amino acid composition of a protein, therefore, is first examined, certain questions immediately come to mind. Is the content of any one or of several amino acids unusually high? Are sulfur-containing amino acids present? Is tryptophan a constituent? What is the distribution of basic and acidic residues? Are uncommon amino acids evident? Is the content of basic amino acids or of aromatic amino acids and leucine high or low?

Relative Amounts of Amino Acids

Of what importance is it if one or more amino acids are present in unusually high amount? This situation does exist. About one in three residues in collagen is glycine; alanine, glycine, and serine constitute more than 85 percent of the residues in the silk fibroin from *Bombyx mori*; and arginine is present to the extent of 65 percent of the residues in certain protamines such as clupeine. Far from simplifying the determination of sequence, the presence of a high percentage of one or several residues actually complicates the work. The likelihood of identical sequences in different parts of the molecule is great, and the placing of these identical sequences may be difficult. For example, the peptide Ser-Gly-Ala-Gly-Ala-Gly as well as many similar peptides such as Ser-Gly, Ala-Gly-Ala-Gly, Gly-Ala, Ala-Gly, etc. may be isolated from certain hydrolysates of silk fibroin (Kay and Schroeder, 1954). In attempting to put together any sequence, one is faced with the question as to whether the fibroin may have a structure such as $(Ser-Gly-Ala-Gly-Ala-Gly)_n$ from which all could derive in one way or another or one such as $(Ser-Gly-Ala-Gly-Ala-Gly)_m$-$(Ala-Gly)_n$-$(Ser-Gly-Ala-Gly)_o$ ... in almost any arrangement. The problem lies in the fact that a specific method for cleaving a protein of such composition is not available, and random cleaving produces such a conglomerate that only the vaguest idea of total sequence can be forthcoming. The protamines in which two of three residues is arginine offer another example; however, the protamines are small, and the sequence has been determined (Chapter 14, p. 173).

Sulfur-containing Amino Acids

What problems are posed by the presence of sulfur-containing amino acids? Only cysteine, cystine, and methionine are commonly encountered. Cysteine and cystine form a redox system, thus,

$$2\text{HSCH}_2\text{CHCOOH} \underset{\text{(Red)}}{\overset{\text{(Oxid)}}{\rightleftharpoons}} \left[-\text{SCH}_2\text{CHCOOH} \right]_2$$

$$\underset{\text{NH}_2}{|} \qquad \qquad \underset{\text{NH}_2}{|}$$

$$\text{Cysteine} \qquad \qquad \text{Cystine}$$

If, then, cysteine is present in a protein, requisite operations in the determination of sequence may cause an oxidation with the formation of structures that are not originally present in the protein. Although it would be desirable to know at the outset of a determination of sequence whether cysteinyl, cystinyl or both types of residues are present, this information frequently is obtained toward the end of the investigation. Accurate analytical procedures can determine the sum of cysteine and cystine in the protein by conversion to one or another derivative. However, the knowledge that one or both may be present allows the investigator to take steps to prevent complications and confusion from arising because of the interconversion of the two. A more detailed discussion of this subject will be given in Chapter 9.

The thioether linkage in methionine is subject to oxidation of a different type than we have seen for cysteine and cystine. The products are first methionine sulfoxides[4] and, on further oxidation, methionine sulfone. The main problem with methionine is likely to arise after a protein has been cleaved to peptides, and their separation is undertaken. If some oxidation of a sample of a methionyl peptide occurs, a mixture of oxidized and unoxidized peptide will be present. If these can be separated, what is actually the same peptide will be isolated in different forms. This may not confuse the determination of sequence but leads to unnecessary labor and loss of material as, for example, in unnecessary analyses after the various forms have been isolated. The solution is to oxidize the methionine to a single form such as methionine sulfone.

---

[4] There are two because sulfoxides are not planar molecules.

This is easily accomplished with performic acid in the cold, and at the same time both cysteine and cystine will be oxidized to cysteic acid (see Chapter 9, p. 94). But what will be the effect on other types of residue? The next question listed above, "Is tryptophan a constituent?," has immediate pertinence because such strenuous conditions of oxidation destroy tryptophan.

This brief discussion shows that the solution of one problem sometimes leads to the formation of another. The lesson to be learned is that the determination of sequence is likely to require that the protein be investigated in several forms such as native, reduced, oxidized, etc., before its complete sequence can be determined.

Content of Basic and Acidic Amino Acids

Of what value can a knowledge of the distribution of basic and acidic amino acids be? This information must be combined with data about the isoelectric point. If the isoelectric point is near neutrality, basic and acidic groups must be present in roughly equal quantities. Suppose, however, that the amino acid composition shows acidic amino acids in twice the number of the basic amino acids. Such a situation would indicate that about half of the acidic amino acids are in the form of asparagine and glutamine.

Uncommon Amino Acids

The presence of uncommon amino acids in a protein must be considered. In addition to the common amino acids in Table 1 (p. 8), other amino acids have been isolated from one or another natural source. Meister (1965) lists many. Most proteins on which intensive investigation of sequence has been done have not contained uncommon amino acids, although desmosine in elastin may be cited as an example. If the amount is large, detection is likely without much difficulty in an ordinary analytical procedure; if it is small, it may well go unobserved.

Content of Basic and Aromatic Amino Acids

Of what importance is the content of basic amino acids or of aromatic amino acids and leucine? It is these amino acids that are involved in hydrolyses with trypsin and chymotrypsin in order to degrade the protein into peptides (Chapter 9). If the content of basic amino acids is low, trypsin will be able to hydrolyze the molecule into relatively few, perhaps rather large, fragments. Likewise, chymotrypsin, which acts mainly on bonds associated with the aromatic amino acids and leucine, will find few bonds to hydrolyze if the content of these is low.

Constituents Other than Amino Acids

Although the amino acid residues are the main components of a protein, other constituents may also be present. Hemocyanin, hemoglobin, and γ-globulin may be cited as examples of a metalloprotein, a heme protein, and a glycoprotein, respectively. Hemocyanin contains copper; hemoglobin contains heme which is an iron porphyrin; and γ-globulin contains carbohydrate.[5] These "extraneous" constituents may be attached covalently or noncovalently and more than one may be present in a given protein. Thus, lactoperoxidase contains a covalently linked heme group and carbohydrate. The presence of such constituents certainly is a portent of future problems—where is a noncovalently linked heme group situated on the molecule or where and how is the carbohydrate attached?

REFERENCES

ALLEN, D. W., W. A. SCHROEDER, AND J. BALOG (1958), Observations on the Chromatographic Heterogeneity of Normal Adult and Fetal Human Hemoglobin: A Study of the Effects of Crystallization and Chromatography on the Heterogeneity and Isoleucine Content, *J. Am. Chem. Soc.*, **80**, 1628.

DIXON, M., AND E. C. WEBB (1964), *Enzymes*, 2nd ed., New York, Academic Press.

HARRIS, J. I., AND C. A. KNIGHT (1955), Studies on the Action of Carboxypeptidase on Tobacco Mosaic Virus, *J. Biol. Chem.*, **214**, 215.

HILL, R. L., D. H. SPACKMAN, D. M. BROWN, AND E. L. SMITH (1958), Leucine Aminopeptidase, *Biochem. Prep.*, **6**, 35.

HIRS, C. H. W., S. MOORE, AND W. H. STEIN (1953), A Chromatographic Investigation of Pancreatic Ribonuclease, *J. Biol. Chem.*, **200**, 493.

KANAREK, L., E. MARLER, R. A. BRADSHAW, R. E. FELLOWS, AND R. L. HILL(1964), The Subunits of Fumarase, *J. Biol. Chem.*, **239**, 4207.

KAY, L. M., AND W. A. SCHROEDER (1954), The Chromatographic Separation and Identification of Some Peptides in Partial Hydrolyzates of Silk Fibroin, *J. Am. Chem. Soc.*, **76**, 3564.

KLOTZ, I. M. (1967), Protein Subunits: A Table, *Science*, **155**, 697.

---

[5] "Glycoprotein" is the generic term for carbohydrate-containing proteins.

KLOTZ, I. M., AND S. KERESZTES-NAGY (1963), Hemerythrin: Molecular Weight and Dissociation into Subunits, *Biochemistry*, **2**, 4451.

MEISTER, A. (1965), *Biochemistry of the Amino Acids*, 2nd ed., New York, Academic Press.

MORRIS, C. J. O. R., AND P. MORRIS (1963), *Separation Methods in Biochemistry*, New York, Interscience.

SANGER, F. (1949), Fractionation of Oxidized Insulin, *Biochem. J.*, **44**, 126.

SCHROEDER, W. A., L. M. KAY, AND I. C. WELLS (1950), Amino Acid Composition of Hemoglobins of Normal Negroes and Sickle-Cell Anemics, *J. Biol. Chem.*, **187**, 221.

SCHROEDER, W. A. (1959), The Chemical Structure of the Normal Human Hemoglobins, *Fortschr. Chem. Org. Naturstoffe*, **17**, 322.

SCHROEDER, W. A., AND R. T. JONES (1965), Some Aspects of the Chemistry and Function of Human and Animal Hemoglobins, *Fortschr. Chem. Org. Naturstoffe*, **23**, 113.

SOBER, H. A., R. W. HARTLEY, JR., W. R. CARROLL, AND E. A. PETERSON (1965), Fractionation of Proteins, in *The Proteins: Composition, Structure, and Function*, 2nd ed., H. Neurath, ed., New York, Academic Press, Vol. III, p. 2.

SUND, H., AND K. WEBER (1966), The Quaternary Structure of Proteins, *Angew. Chem.* (International Ed.), **5**, 231.

5

THE DETERMINATION OF
AMINO ACID COMPOSITION

Some of the discussion in earlier chapters has assumed that the investigator has available a detailed and exact knowledge of the amino acid composition of the protein—a knowledge that will influence the choice of experiments. However, information about amino acid composition is required both for the entire protein and for the peptides that are produced in various experiments. The amino acid composition of a peptide will reveal its size and also dictate to a degree the type of experiments that should help in determining its sequence. The amino acid composition of protein and peptides serves the purpose of maintaining a material balance as the investigation proceeds to its ultimate goal of sequence determination. This chapter will outline briefly the historical development of methods for the determination of amino acid composition, describe modern methods for its accomplishment, and consider limitations and problems.

HISTORICAL DEVELOPMENT

From the time that glycine was first isolated from gelatin by Braconnot in 1820 until the present time when a new amino acid may be discovered, the determination has changed from the qualitative to the quantitative and from a lengthy, time-consuming process of months and years to one that may be completed in a few hours.

As knowledge about proteins increased and more amino acids were detected, attempts at quantitative determination began. We have already mentioned in Chapter 1 the ester distillation method of Fischer for the neutral amino acids and the precipitation method of Kossel for the basic amino acids. Foreman devised means for determining the acidic amino acids. These methods required large amounts of protein. Other methods, specific colorimetric reactions for example, began to be developed. More sensitive, they were of limited applicability because not all amino acids give a specific color test. Then followed the widely applicable "microbiological" procedures which depended upon the growth response of a microorganism to the quantity of a given amino acid in the medium. Although procedures for all of the amino acids were available in the early 1940s, they were so laborious that few complete analyses of a protein were ever made. Most of these were composites of results from several laboratories; Brand (1946) was the first to report the complete analysis of a protein—β-lactoglobulin—from a single laboratory by a complex of methods.

Just before the dawn of the modern era of methods for amino acid analysis, a meeting at the New York Academy of Sciences in 1945 discussed in detail the state of the art at that time. The publication that resulted (Stein *et al.*, 1946) is an excellent history of the development of methods of amino acid analysis.

Moore and Stein ushered in the modern era of analysis when in 1948 they described a rapid, accurate, and precise chromatographic method that required only a few milligrams for a single complete analysis (Stein and Moore, 1948; Moore and Stein, 1948 and 1949). The present-day ability to carry out a determination of sequence derives in no small measure from the further elaboration of methods by these workers and their colleagues. The chromatographic procedures permitted the separation of the amino acids, and a quantitative colorimetric method allowed their determination. The principles of this colorimetric method will be discussed first.

THE NINHYDRIN METHOD FOR THE COLORIMETRIC DETERMINATION OF AMINO ACIDS

That a colorimetric method is nonspecific is of no moment if the compounds can be separated and qualitatively identified. Indeed, it is advantageous because a single reagent suffices. Many years ago, Ruhemann showed that amino acids and ninhydrin react with great sensitivity to give a purple compound now known as "Ruhemann's Purple" (West, 1965). The over-all reaction is shown in Reaction Scheme 1.

The exact course of the reaction is dependent on the pH. Although the aldehyde and carbon dioxide are formed over the useful range of pH, Ruhemann's Purple is produced only at a pH near 5, whereas hydrindantin which may be formulated as follows and ammonia result at pH 2.5.

$$H_3N^{\oplus}-CHR-CO_2^{\ominus} + 2$$ [Ninhydrin structure] $\xrightarrow{\text{pH 5}}$

Ninhydrin
(Triketohydrindene hydrate)
(2,2-Dihydroxy-1,3-indandione)

$$R-CHO +$$ [Ruhemann's Purple structure] $$+ CO_2$$

Ruhemann's Purple
(Diketohydrindylidene-diketohydrindamine)
(Indandione-2-N-2'-indanone enolate)

Reaction Scheme 1.

The release and measurement of carbon dioxide was the basis of the useful gasometric method of van Slyke and co-workers (1941) for the quantitative (not qualitative) estimation of amino acids. The present-day usefulness of ninhydrin lies almost exclusively in the sensitivity of the color reaction.

Although various proposals as to the mechanism of the production of Ruhemann's Purple have been made, the current idea which has been summarized by McCaldin (1960) is depicted in Reaction Scheme 2.

The sensitivity of the color reaction had led to repeated unsuccessful attempts to devise a quantitative colorimetric method that would be as accurate and precise as the gasometric method of van Slyke. Moore and Stein (1948) solved the problem by adding hydrindantin to the reagent either directly or by reducing part of the ninhydrin with stannous chloride. On the basis of the proposed mechanism, it is not immediately obvious how the hydrindantin enters into the reaction to make it more quantitative.

For quantitative purposes, the reaction is carried out in practice at pH 5–5.5 at 100°C for 10 to 15 min in a buffered solution that contains, in addition to ninhydrin and hydrindantin, an organic solvent to keep the organic compounds in solution. A specific recipe for the reagent will be given in the next section.

The various amino acids produce neither the theoretical amount of color in this reaction nor an equal amount of color per mole. Nevertheless, the procedure can be used quantitatively because they yield

Reaction Scheme 2.

reproducible results and because the color is in direct proportion to the amount of amino acid. For each amino acid, therefore, a standard curve or a calculating factor must be determined. Despite these limitations, the precision and accuracy of the procedure are of the order of ± 2 percent.

Although the *amino* acids form Ruhemann's Purple under appropriate conditions, the *imino* acids proline and hydroxyproline give only a yellow-brown product, which is thought to have the following structure

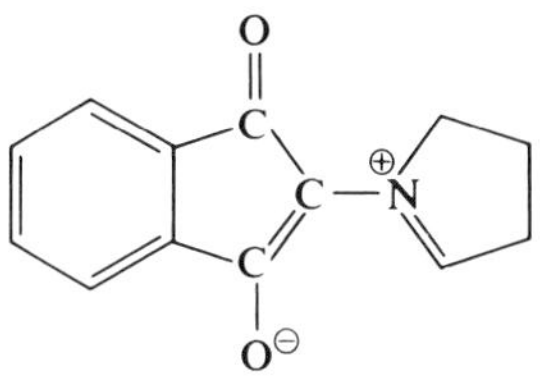

The reaction of ninhydrin with proline and hydroxyproline is far less sensitive than that with the amino acids because the maximum molar absorptivity of the product is much smaller than that of Ruhemann's Purple.

The ninhydrin reaction is valuable, of course, not only for such quantitative work but also for detecting spots of amino acids and peptides after paper chromatography or electrophoresis. The dried paper is simply dipped in or sprayed with a solution of ninhydrin in some organic solvent and the color is developed at room temperature or by heating[1]. If certain chemicals such as substituted pyridines are added to the reagent, the spots of some amino acids have distinctive colors that aid in qualitative identification. The ninhydrin reaction is also applied quantitatively to paper chromatography in various ways: visual comparison with the color produced by known amounts; photometric comparison with standards; elution of the colored products and spectrophotometry; elution, development of color, and spectrophotometry; etc.

QUANTITATIVE AMINO ACID ANALYSIS BY ION-EXCHANGE CHROMATOGRAPHY ON COLUMNS

The first quantitative chromatographic method of amino acid analysis that was described by Moore and Stein used starch columns with several types of developer (Stein and Moore, 1948; Moore and

---

[1] The number of procedures that have been described for this purpose is almost as numerous as the investigators who have used the reagent.

Stein, 1949). By means of a collector, the effluent was divided automatically into small fractions to which the ninhydrin reaction was then applied quantitatively. Complete analysis required approximately 12 days (if the three necessary chromatograms were run consecutively) and 800–900 individual ninhydrin analyses. The method was described in meticulous detail and gave results that were accurate to ± 3 percent in control tests.

The starch method was superseded by an ion-exchange procedure of equivalent accuracy and about equal speed. It had the distinct advantage that entirely aqueous solutions could be used[2] and that each column could be readied for the next analysis by simple regeneration without repouring. Continued improvement and modification led finally in 1958 to the description of an automatic amino acid analyzer by means of which a complete analysis could be made in less than 24 hr (Spackman, Stein, and Moore, 1958). Because an automatic amino acid analyzer is no longer a luxury but a necessity in sequence determination, it is worthwhile to describe the apparatus and procedure in some detail. However, because modification and improvement are continually being made, this description will be outmoded in some details before this volume appears in print.

The principle of automatic amino acid analysis is shown in outline in Fig. 11. After the sample has been applied quantitatively to the column and rinsed in, the developer is pumped through the column at a constant rate. The effluent from the column is met by a stream of ninhydrin reagent, which likewise is pumped at a constant rate. To produce color in any portion of the effluent that contains amino acids, the mixture is then passed through a long coil, which is heated in a boiling water bath. The heated reaction mixture finally passes through a three-cell photoelectric photometer whose output is displayed on a three-channel recorder with inks of different color (represented in Fig. 11 with different types of line). Quantitative calculation can be made from this record.

The details of the method described below are those of the original automatic procedure. Modifications that have given greater speed and increased sensitivity and that will be mentioned have not altered the basic concept or the machinery and plumbing of the apparatus.

Two sizes of chromatographic column were used: with the smaller (0.9 × 15 cm), the basic amino acids and ammonia as well as tryptophan, if present, were determined, whereas with the larger (0.9 × 150 cm) the

---

[2] Because the starch method used developers that contained organic solvents, essentially all salts had to be excluded from the sample in order to prevent distortion of the zones. The same is true for paper chromatograms.

remaining common amino acids were separated. The packing for these columns was a sulfonated polystyrene cation-exchange resin of the type described in Table 3, Chapter 3. The average particle size of resin for the smaller (generally termed "the short") column was 30 μ and for the larger ("the long") column was 40 μ. Developer was passed through

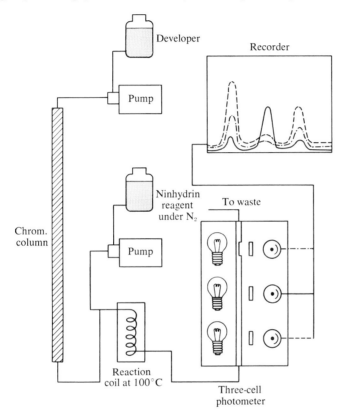

Figure 11. Principles of automatic amino acid analysis (not to scale). See text for discussion.

either column at 30 ml per hr while the temperature was maintained at 50°C. The short column required about 4 hr for completion and the long column about 16 hr. Consequently, the chromatogram on the short column was begun in the morning and that on the long column immediately thereafter. At the completion of the long column, the apparatus was turned off automatically.

The greatest modification of procedure has been made in the size of the columns, the resins, and the flow rate of developer. The short column has been reduced in dimension to 0.9×5 cm and the long column to 0.9×60 cm. Continued improvement has produced uniform spherical resins. These resins have less resistance to flow, and consequently somewhat smaller particle size and faster rate of solvent flow can be used without undue increase in back pressure. The rate of development has more than doubled to about 70 ml per hr. Even at this increased rate of flow, the resolution of the amino acids on these shorter columns is as good or better than on the longer columns because of the uniform and smaller particle size of the ion exchanger. Consequently, because of increase in flow rate and decrease in size, the short column may be completed in less than an hour and the long column in about $2\frac{1}{2}$ hr. As a result, three short columns and two long columns may be finished in the course of a normal working day, and the third long column may be started and allowed to shut down automatically at completion. Many of these modifications have been the result of keen competition among the several manufacturers of amino acid analyzers. Some of the commercial analyzers use the two-column system of Moore and Stein, which was originally devised because the basic amino acids required much time to emerge from the column and did not give quantitative results. Single-column procedures have since been devised, and one is incorporated in a commercial analyzer that uses five 0.63×75-cm columns. After a sample has been applied to each column, an automatic programming device completes consecutive analyses and regenerates the columns so that they are ready for use on the next day.

The two-column procedure has been accelerated almost without alteration in conditions of development. The sample is dissolved in a known volume of buffer (citrate with $0.2N$ sodium ion concentration adjusted to pH 2.2 with acid), and an aliquot portion is applied to each column and rinsed in with developer. The short-column developer is a citrate buffer at pH 5.28, which is $0.35N$ in sodium ion. Under these conditions, acidic and neutral amino acids in the sample are virtually unretarded and emerge in a single peak. If tryptophan is present, it emerges next to be followed by lysine, histidine, ammonia, and arginine. Development of the long column is started with buffer of pH 3.25 and $0.2N$ sodium ion concentration. The amino acids emerge in the following order: aspartic acid, threonine, serine, glutamic acid, proline, glycine, alanine, cystine, valine, methionine, isoleucine, leucine, tyrosine, and phenylalanine. The latter five amino acids are eluted very slowly with the indicated buffer so that an automatic change is made to a similar buffer at pH 4.25. The time of the change will depend somewhat on the geometry of the system and may be arranged so that the influence of the second developer becomes effective either before or after the valine emerges from the column. The short column need be regenerated only infrequently, but the long column is first washed with 0.2N sodium hydroxide to remove the basic amino acids and then with the starting developer (pH 3.25). In single-column procedures, somewhat similar developers are used either stepwise (Dus *et al.*, 1966) or in a gradient (Piez and Morris, 1960; Hamilton, 1963).

The ninhydrin reagent is usually pumped into the system at half the speed of the developer. As originally devised for the automatic procedure, the ninhydrin reagent contained 20 g of ninhydrin and 0.4 g of stannous chloride dihydrate in a liter of solvent composed of three parts by volume of methyl cellosolve (monomethyl ether of ethylene glycol) and one part by volume of 4M acetate buffer at pH 5.5. This reagent is still satisfactory, although some modifications have been made to simplify its preparation. When prepared and stored under oxygen-free nitrogen in the dark, the reagent is stable for some weeks at room temperature and indefinitely at 5°C.

Adequate and reproducible though not necessarily complete color development occurs during the approximately 10 min that the solution requires to pass through the heated Teflon coil, which has an inner diameter of approximately 0.7 mm and a length of about 30 m.

From the coil, the solution passes through the photometer. Ruhemann's Purple has an absorption maximum at 570 mμ, which is used for the determination. The photometer is designed to make readings through two thicknesses of solution at 570 mμ. This is made necessary by the diverse quantities of the amino acids in a protein. For instance, on a molar basis the amino acids may be present in a protein hydrolyzate in a ratio of 20:1. The amount of color and roughly the heights of the peaks on the chromatogram will also differ by this ratio. Accordingly, if the amount of sample is adjusted so that the smaller component gives an adequate peak for precise calculation, the larger component will give so large a peak that there are technical problems in making a precise calculation. On the other hand, if the sample is adjusted to the larger component, the peak of the smaller may be so small that calculation may be inexact. However, when reading is made on two thicknesses of solution, which differ usually by about a factor of three, the quantity of small components can be calculated from the peak that is produced by the greater thickness and vice versa. The photometer also makes readings at 440 mμ, because at this wavelength the yellow-brown products of proline and hydroxyproline with ninhydrin have maximum absorption.

The output of the photometer traces three curves of absorbance vs. time (hence also effluent volume) on the three-channel recorder: one

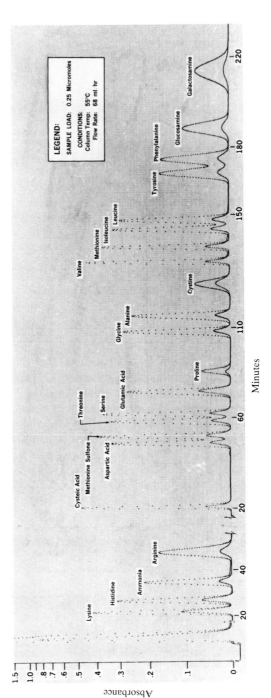

Figure 12. Automatic amino acid analysis of a synthetic mixture of amino acids. The basic amino acids and ammonia were separated on a 0.9 × 5-cm column, and the acidic and neutral amino acids on a 0.9 × 57-cm column. An accelerated procedure with spherical resins was used. [Source: Benson and Patterson, *Anal. Chem.,* **37,** 1108 (1965). Copyright 1965 by the American Chemical Society. Reprinted by permission of the copyright owner.]

each for a normal thickness of solution at 570 and 440 mμ and one for the lesser thickness at 570 mμ.

By altering the design of the photometer and by electronic modification of the recorder, it has been possible to increase the sensitivity of the ion exchange procedures so that only a few nanomoles (10^{-9} moles) of an amino acid may be quantitatively determined. Hamilton (1965) has estimated the amino acids in a human fingerprint in a beaker! Speed and sensitivity have been increased without sacrifice of accuracy and precision. Because a single amino acid analyzer can make three to six analyses per day, the burden of calculation can be troublesome. As a result, automatic integration from the recorder and calculation by computer have been devised.

Quantitative estimation of amino acids by ion-exchange procedures requires that a standard mixture of amino acids be chromatographed. From the record, an appropriate constant for each amino acid is calculated. The reproducibility of these constants is dependent to a large degree upon the care with which the ninhydrin reagent is prepared and stored. Successive preparations of reagent usually give constants within ± 2 percent.

Calculation is made by integration of the recorded curve. If the recorder prints dots instead of drawing a solid line, integration may be done by counting the dots in the upper half of the curve and multiplying by the net absorbance of the peak. From a standard chromatogram with known quantities of amino acids, constants dependent on such factors as the kind of amino acid, the length of the photometer cells, and the printing speed of the recorder are obtained; the amount of amino acid in the analysis of an unknown sample may be calculated by dividing the product of dots and net absorbance by the appropriate constant.

Figure 12 is a typical example of a record of an automatic amino acid analysis. Depicted is the separation of the common amino acids in a protein hydrolyzate. This powerful method also permits the separation of such derivatives as cysteic acid, aminoethylcysteine, carboxymethylcysteine, and the like. The elution behaviors of many more ninhydrin-positive compounds have been reported. Zacharius and Talley (1962) have described the chromatographic properties of 90 compounds, and Hamilton (1963) has described those of 186. If so many compounds were present in a single complex mixture, the chromatogram would by no means be able to separate each component into a single distinct peak. However, this knowledge of their chromatographic behavior may be utilized to gain some insight into the identity of unanticipated peaks that may appear in the hydrolyzates of proteins or during the analysis of biological fluids such as urine, blood plasma, plant extracts, etc.

It is apparent from Fig. 12 that an excellent separation of all of the common amino acids takes place under these conditions. Despite the fact that an ion-exchange resin is used as the stationary phase, ion exchange is certainly not the only factor responsible for the efficacy of the separation. To be sure, in a broad sense the acidic, neutral, and basic amino acids emerge from the column in the order in which one would expect. However, on the basis of acid-base characteristics alone, the separation of glycine, alanine, valine, isoleucine, and leucine would hardly be expected: these five amino acids have virtually identical values of pK_1' and pK_2'. The selectivity of the procedure must, therefore, involve the side chain in some way. As a further example of the sensitivity of separation, it should be mentioned that the diastereoisomeric pairs of isoleucine and alloisoleucine, threonine and allothreonine, and hydroxyproline and allohydroxyproline may be separated, although the enantiomorphs of an amino acid cannot be.

The methods have now been used for the analysis of many proteins. As an example, the results of their application to the analysis of swine heart fumarase are cited in Table 5 (Kanarek and Hill, 1964). The data illustrate very well a number of features of amino acid analysis. The amino acids are listed in the order of their emergence from the short and long columns, respectively; this is now a common way of listing. The sum of the amino acids accounted for 100.5 percent of the dry weight of the samples. Such an excellent recovery is an indication of the absence of other constituents such as carbohydrates. Expression of the data in terms of residues per molecular weight rather than as grams per 100 g of protein, for example, makes it easy to inspect the data and to calculate and compare the relative amounts of the various residues. The precision of duplicate determinations in individual hydrolyzates as well as the agreement at various times of hydrolysis is consistent and generally better than the accuracy of ± 3 percent that is to be expected of the method. The analysis also points up the individualistic behavior of proteins. Ordinarily, threonine is destroyed to the extent of about 5 percent per 24 hr of hydrolysis but, in this instance, no such destruction is apparent. On the other hand, serine exhibits the normal approximate loss of 10 percent per 24 hr and also its frequently erratic behavior. Although valine often appears in greater amount as the time of hydrolysis is extended, this also is not evident here. Inasmuch as fumarase may have four identical subunits, the composition of each subunit would be one-fourth that in Table 5. Although not all of the numbers are exactly divisible by four as given, they in fact are if the precision of the data is

TABLE 5. *The Amino Acid Composition of Swine Heart Fumarase*

Amino acid	\multicolumn{4}{c}{Residues per molecule[a] after hydrolysis for}
	24 hr[b]	48 hr[b]	72 hr[b]	Calculated
Lysine	129	128	131	129
Histidine	52	56	53	54
Arginine	55	53	54	54
Aspartic Acid	177	175	179	177
Threonine	99	98	100	100
Serine	84	66	71	92[c]
Glutamic Acid	174	174	175	174
Proline	81	80	80	80
Glycine	142	143	143	143
Alanine	202	197	200	200
Cystine/2	12.5[d]			12
Valine	128	132	132	131
Methionine	61	61	63	62
Isoleucine	95	97	98	97
Leucine	148	147	147	147
Tyrosine	38	35	37	40[c]
Phenylalanine	66	59	63	63
Tryptophan				8[e]
Ammonia				170[f]

[a] Based on a molecular weight of 194,000.
[b] Duplicate analyses were performed at each time of hydrolysis. Except for serine the results were consistent to ± 3 percent.
[c] By extrapolation to zero time of hydrolysis.
[d] Measured as cysteic acid after performic acid oxidation.
[e] By colorimetry and spectrophotometric analysis.
[f] Calculated on the assumption that the electric charge was zero at pH 7.95.
[SOURCE: Kanarek and Hill, *J. Biol. Chem.*, **239**, 4202 (1964)].

considered. Alanine would be present to the extent of 50 residues per subunit; the final accounting when the sequence is known may be expected to lie within 50 ± 2 residues. However, cystine/2 and tryptophan at three and two residues per subunit, respectively, are not likely to be in error.

QUANTITATIVE AMINO ACID ANALYSIS BY GAS CHROMATOGRAPHY

Gas chromatographic methods in general are rapid and require minute amounts of material for analysis. Many commercial instruments are available with a wide variety and sensitivity of detecting systems, special contols such as temperature programming, etc. In view of the constant improvement in amino acid analysis as described above, as well as the desire and need for more and more rapid analysis, it is to be expected that gas chromatography might be resorted to as further means to these ends.

In any application of gas chromatography to amino acid analysis, the obstacle to be overcome is the involatility of these compounds. None of the common amino acids melts below 180°C, and melting usually occurs with decomposition. Although gas chromatography can be carried out at rather high temperatures, its application to the amino acids themselves seems to be a goal unlikely of achievement. Attention has, therefore, been given to the search for stable and suitably volatile derivatives. In general, volatility has been achieved by acylation of the amino group and esterification of the carboxyl group. Various investigators have used a variety of reagents for these purposes. One of the more successful procedures that has been described is that of Gehrke and co-workers (Gehrke *et al.*, 1965; Lamkin and Gehrke, 1965; Gehrke and Shahrokhi, 1966; Stalling and Gehrke, 1966) who react amino acids first with *n*-butanol by transesterification and then with trifluoroacetic anhydride according to Reaction Scheme 3 to give the

$$R\text{—}CH\text{—}COO^{\ominus} + CH_3OH \xrightarrow[\substack{HCl \\ 30\ min}]{\substack{Room \\ temp.}} R\text{—}CH\text{—}COOCH_3 + H_2O$$

with $NH_3^{\oplus}$ on the left and $NH_3^{\oplus}Cl^{\ominus}$ on the right, plus *n*-BuOH (HCl, 90°C, 3 hr)

$$R\text{—}CH\text{—}COOBu \xleftarrow[\substack{Room \\ temp. \\ 2\ hr}]{CH_2Cl_2} (F_3CCO)_2O + R\text{—}CH\text{—}COOBu \ (+\ CH_3OH)$$

with $HN\text{—}COCF_3$ on the left and $NH_3^{\oplus}Cl^{\ominus}$ on the right

Reaction Scheme 3.

n-butyl-N-trifluoroacetyl derivative. All amino acids have derivatives that are satisfactorily volatile, although tryptophan and arginine in early experiments presented some problems. After the derivatives have been prepared, the gas chromatographic separation requires only 75 min. An analysis of a hydrolyzate of bovine serum albumin by this method is shown in Fig. 13. The weight of amino acids for each chromatogram was only 25 μg. Application of such a system of analysis to actual problems of sequence determination has yet to be made. The speed of

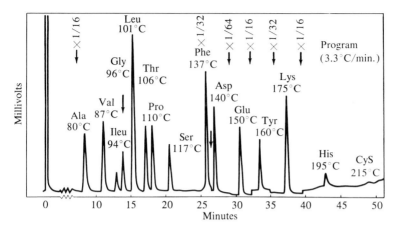

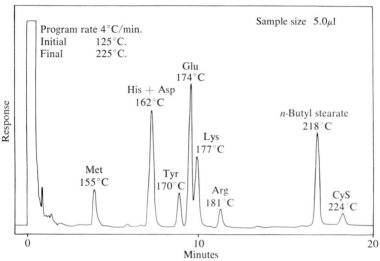

Figure 13. An analysis of bovine serum albumin by gas chromatography of the *n*-butyl-N-trifluoroacetyl derivatives. The columns were 4 mm × 100 cm and each had a different type of packing (through the courtesy of Professor C. W. Gehrke).

the chromatographic step, which may be attractive to many workers, is at least partially offset by the time that is required to prepare the derivative (even though the concurrent preparation of several samples reduces the overall time per sample). Analysis by ion-exchange chromatography has become widespread and entrenched. Gas chromatographic methods will not be able to challenge its position easily.

QUANTITATIVE AMINO ACID ANALYSIS BY PAPER METHODS

Paper chromatography requires a minimum of both equipment and material. Indeed, it was with qualitative and roughly quantitative paper methods almost exclusively that Sanger and collaborators were able to determine the amino acid sequence of insulin. Paper chromatography or electrophoresis, therefore, has had very extensive application both qualitatively and quantitatively in protein chemistry. The many published procedures attest to the fact that the quantitative determination of amino acids by paper methods with the accuracy and precision of column chromatographic methods is not an easy task. There seem to be few papers in which the author is willing to concede that any procedure other than his own has real merit. Consequently, the potential user of a paper procedure will find a virtually endless selection of solvent systems for separating the amino acids by chromatography in one or two dimensions and a wide variety of methods for making the final quantitative determination. As a single example of paper methods, an electrophoretic method of Dreyer and Bynum (1967) may be considered; others may be found in any text on chromatography. The separations that are shown in Fig. 14 were achieved by electrophoresis at pH 1.58 along a 200-cm length of Whatman 3 MM paper at 7,800 V for 115 min at 43–44°C. The equipment is rather different from that of Fig. 7 (p. 29). A large tank is constructed with a partition at the bottom to divide this part into two electrode vessels which are filled with buffer. The remainder of the tank is filled with an inert high boiling petroleum distillate. The paper, which is thoroughly saturated with buffer, is supported on a frame in this inert solvent. Each end of the paper dips into an electrode vessel for electrical contact. After electrophoresis, drying, and development of color with ninhydrin and cadmium acetate under specific conditions, the quantitative determination is made by cutting the paper into strips and scanning each with a recording densitometer. This method is reported to be accurate to ± 10 percent.

In view of the difficulty that investigators have clearly had in reproducing the well-described procedures of others for the quantitative paper chromatographic determination of amino acids, it is probable that, if a paper method is to equal a column method in precision and accuracy, the care, equipment, and time may be equal to or greater than those required for column methods. For example, Hanes and co-workers (1961) have made a detailed study of apparatus and conditions of paper chromatography; their description covers 75 pages.

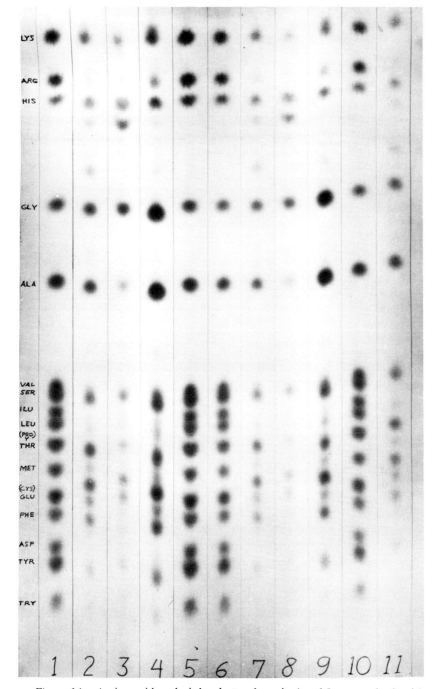

Figure 14. Amino acid analysis by electrophoresis. 1 and 5 are standards with 20 nanomoles of each amino acid, and 6 and 10 are standards with 10 nanomoles. The other samples were normal or pathological urine specimens. Other details are given in the text (through the courtesy of Professor W. J. Dreyer).

QUANTITATIVE AMINO ACID ANALYSIS BY OTHER METHODS

From time to time, other methods of quantitative analysis of amino acids have been used. For example, amino acids may be converted to DNP or PTH derivatives (Chapter 6), separated by some method, and quantitatively estimated. The procedures generally require correction factors and have seen limited application.

PROCEDURES PREPARATORY TO AMINO ACID ANALYSIS

The above description should suggest to the reader that, given a mixture of amino acids, the determination of the composition both qualitatively and quantitatively poses no great problems. This is, indeed, the case; the procedures that precede the amino acid analysis may be a source of greater error than the analysis itself. Let us consider the operations preliminary to an analysis [discussed in detail by Light and Smith (1963)].

Assume that the isolation of a protein has produced a "pure" substance. An elementary analysis of the material is worthwhile mainly for elements such as nitrogen, sulfur, phosphorus, and specific elements (iron, for example, in the heme proteins). This information permits the analyst to keep a material balance of the protein accounted for in terms of amino acids found. A determination of ash at this point would prove or disprove whether all contaminating salts had been removed (except, of course, for such proteins of which they are constituents—iron in the heme proteins again or zinc in insulin). Because proteins are hygroscopic substances, it is usually inconvenient to take a dried weighed portion for analysis but rather to determine the moisture content of the material and to correct for its presence.

An effective and common way to cleave a protein to a mixture of amino acids is to hydrolyze in acid, a procedure that is now almost 150 years old and was first performed by Braconnot. A minimum of alteration and destruction occurs if a few milligrams of protein (enough for several analyses) are hydrolyzed in 1 or 2 ml of glass-distilled $6N$ hydrochloric acid in an evacuated sealed tube for 24 hr at 110°C. Certain conditions are of importance. The dilute solution (usually less than 0.5 percent) decreases destructive reactions, for example, between the carbohydrate portion of a glycoprotein and the amino acids. Many early day hydrolyses in 10- to 20-percent solutions produced black insoluble "humin." Distillation of acid removes contaminating trace metals that might catalyze destructive reactions, and evacuation prevents oxidative alteration (for example, of methionine). Hydrochloric acid is the acid of choice largely because it can be removed easily by evaporation.

When a known quantity of protein has been hydrolyzed in this way, when the acid has been removed rapidly in a stream of air or in vacuo, and when the residue has been dissolved in a definite volume of solvent and a portion has been analyzed by column chromatographic methods, it may be expected that the content of aspartic acid, glutamic acid, proline, glycine, alanine, methionine, tyrosine, phenylalanine, lysine, histidine, and arginine will be accurately revealed. What then of the asparagine, glutamine, valine, isoleucine, leucine, threonine, serine, tryptophan, cysteine, and cystine? Are the contents of almost half the amino acids subject to considerable error in their determination because of hydrolytic problems? Let us consider these ten amino acids in various groups. Asparagine and glutamine are quantitatively hydrolyzed to aspartic and glutamic acids and are determined accurately as such after acid hydrolysis; whether the acid or its amide is present is usually not decided at this stage of investigation. Amino acids such as valine, isoleucine, and leucine, which have bulky aliphatic side chains, have been shown to be released more slowly from peptide linkage than are other residues. Even they are likely to be almost completely released in 24 hr of hydrolysis. The completeness actually will depend on sequences in the protein (a valyl-valyl bond is particularly resistant[3]).

The problem of incomplete hydrolysis is easily solved by hydrolyzing other samples of protein for longer and longer periods of time and determining when the content of these amino acids reaches a constant amount. Usually, 48 to 72 hr is an adequate length of time. On the other hand, little, if any, of the tryptophan will survive even a 24-hr hydrolysis, and it will be observed that the content of serine and threonine decreases as the time of hydrolysis is lengthened. Ordinarily, about 10 percent of the serine and 5 percent of the threonine are destroyed in 24 hr of hydrolysis; because the destruction varies somewhat from protein to protein, an accurate determination of the content of these amino acids requires the estimation of their destruction as a function of time and correction to zero time either by a linear extrapolation or, if the data warrant it, by the use of first-order kinetics. The quantity of tryptophan can be determined by several methods. Because

---

[3] If one valyl-valyl bond exists in a total of 20 valyl residues in a protein and is hydrolyzed to the extent of 75 percent while all other valyl bonds are hydrolyzed to 95 percent, the determined content of valine will still be 18.6 residues or 93 percent of the total.

tryptophan has an absorption maximum at about 290 mμ, methods have been devised for its spectrophotometric estimation in solutions of the intact protein. In addition, various specific colorimetric procedures have been developed. Although many amino acids are completely or partially destroyed by alkaline hydrolysis, tryptophan is not. Consequently, after alkaline hydrolysis, the usual analytical methods, such as column chromatography, can be applied. Whether cysteine and/or cystine are present may not be resolved finally until the entire sequence is known. The sum of the two may be determined with relative ease either after oxidation with performic acid to cysteic acid (discussed further in Chapter 9, p. 94) or after reduction and reaction with ethylenimine to form β-aminoethylcysteine (see Chapter 9, p. 96), both of which are easily determined after hydrolysis. Methods for distinguishing cysteine and cystine will be taken up in Chapter 13, p. 160.

It will be apparent from the above that, with due consideration for the properties of the various amino acids, an amino acid analysis should yield results which are limited mainly by the analytical procedures themselves. Vagaries of particular amino acids in specific circumstances can usually be detected when the composition is studied as a function of the time of hydrolysis. The effects of the rather drastic conditions of hydrolysis could be eliminated potentially by enzymatic hydrolysis. Although such methods have been described (Hill and Schmidt, 1962), they have had limited application largely because the enzymes are not readily available. They have the advantage that the amide groups of glutamine and asparagine are not hydrolyzed, and that serine, threonine, and tryptophan are not partially or completely destroyed.

Despite some of the problems in preparing an acceptable hydrolyzate, it can reasonably be expected that a careful analysis will give answers with an accuracy of the order of ±5 percent or better for each amino acid. Thus, if a particular amino acid is present to the extent of 15 to 20 residues in a protein, we can expect to know its content to ±1 residue. Obviously, if only 4 residues are present, an error of ±5 percent is only ±0.2 residues and is not likely to be misleading. This goal has been realized in the case of several proteins whose entire sequence has been determined: in several instances of proteins with about 150 residues, the original analysis has been correct to ±2 to 4 residues.

THE REPRESENTATION OF AMINO ACID COMPOSITION

The results of an amino acid analysis may be and have been presented in many ways. Frequently, data are expressed as grams of amino acid per 100 g of protein. In this usage, the sum of all the amino acid contents will be greater than 100 g because of the water that ruptured every peptide bond. This information can be converted easily to grams of residue per 100 g of protein; thus,

$$\text{g amino acid per 100 g} \times \frac{\text{MW of amino acid} - \text{MW of water}}{\text{MW of amino acid}}.$$

The sum of all the grams of residue per 100 g of protein is a measure of the protein accounted for by the analysis (the material balance). Other less useful ways express composition as grams of nitrogen per 100 g of nitrogen or percent nitrogen of the total nitrogen.

For one who is interested in sequence, composition is probably most usefully expressed in terms of the number of residues of each amino acid per molecular weight of the protein as in Table 5 (or some arbitrary molecular weight such as 100,000 if the actual molecular weight is not known). This method of presenting the data shows at a glance whether a protein is high or low in content of a given residue. It is almost the only practical way of expressing the amino acid composition of a peptide, which usually is not weighed before hydrolysis and for which only a knowledge of the kind and relative amount of the various residues is desired.

REFERENCES

BRAND, E. (1946), Amino Acid Composition of Simple Proteins, *Ann. N.Y. Acad. Sci.*, **47**, 187.

DREYER, W. J., AND E. BYNUM (1967), High-Voltage Paper Electrophoresis, in *Enzyme Structure* (Vol. 11 of *Methods in Enzymology*), C. H. W. Hirs, ed., New York, Academic Press, p. 32.

DUS, K., S. LINDROTH, R. PABST, AND R. M. SMITH (1966), Continuous Amino Acid Analysis: Elution Programming and Automatic Column Selection by Means of a Rotating Valve, *Anal. Biochem.*, **14**, 41.

GEHRKE, C. W., W. M. LAMKIN, D. L. STALLING, AND F. SHAHROKHI (1965), Quantitative Gas Chromatography of Amino Acids, *Biochem. Biophys. Res. Commun.*, **19**, 328.

GEHRKE, C. W., AND F. SHAHROKHI (1966), Chromatographic Separation of *n*-Butyl-N-Trifluoroacetyl Esters of Amino Acids, *Anal. Biochem.*, **15**, 97.

HAMILTON, P. B. (1963), Ion Exchange Chromatography of Amino Acids. A Single Column, High Resolving, Fully Automatic Procedure, *Anal. Chem.*, **35**, 2055.

HAMILTON, P. B. (1965), Amino-acids on Hands, *Nature*, **205**, 284.

HANES, C. S., AND COLLABORATORS (1961), Quantitative Chromatographic Methods. Parts 2, 3, and 4, *Can. J. Biochem. Physiol.*, **39**, 119.

HILL, R. L., AND W. R. SCHMIDT (1962), The Complete Enzymic Hydrolysis of Proteins, *J. Biol. Chem.*, **237**, 389.

KANAREK, L., AND R. L. HILL (1964), The Preparation and Characterization of Fumarase from Swine Heart Muscle, *J. Biol. Chem.*, **239**, 4202.

LAMKIN, W. M., AND C. W. GEHRKE (1965), Quantitative Gas Chromatography of Amino Acids. Preparation of *n*-Butyl-N-Trifluoroacetyl Esters, *Anal. Chem.*, **37**, 383.

LIGHT, A., AND E. L. SMITH (1963), Amino Acid Analysis of Peptides and Proteins, in *The Proteins: Composition, Structure, and Function*, 2nd ed., H. Neurath, ed., New York, Academic Press, Vol. I, p. 2.

MC CALDIN, D. J. (1960), The Chemistry of Ninhydrin, *Chem. Rev.*, **60**, 39.

MOORE, S., AND W. H. STEIN (1948), Photometric Ninhydrin Method for Use in the Chromatography of Amino Acids, *J. Biol. Chem.*, **176**, 367.

MOORE, S., AND W. H. STEIN (1949), Chromatography of Amino Acids on Starch Columns. Solvent Mixtures for the Fractionation of Protein Hydrolyzates, *J. Biol. Chem.*, **178**, 53.

PIEZ, K., AND L. MORRIS (1960), A Modified Procedure for the Automatic Analysis of Amino Acids, *Anal. Biochem.*, **1**, 187.

SPACKMAN, D. H., W. H. STEIN, AND S. MOORE (1958), Automatic Recording Apparatus for Use in the Chromatography of Amino Acids, *Anal. Chem.*, **30**, 1190.

STALLING, D. L., AND C. W. GEHRKE (1966), Quantitative Analysis of Amino Acids by Gas Chromatography: Acylation of Arginine, *Biochem. Biophys. Res. Commun.*, **22**, 329.

STEIN, W. H., ET AL. (1946), Amino Acid Analysis of Proteins, *Ann. N. Y. Acad. Sci.*, **47**, 57–240.

STEIN, W. H., AND S. MOORE (1948), Chromatography of Amino Acids on Starch Columns. Separation of Phenylalanine, Leucine, Isoleucine, Methionine, Tyrosine, and Valine, *J. Biol. Chem.*, **176**, 337.

VAN SLYKE, D. D., R. T. DILLON, D. A. MACFADYEN, AND P. HAMILTON (1941), Gasometric Determination of Carboxyl Groups in Free Amino Acids, *J. Biol. Chem.*, **141**, 627.

WEST, R. (1965), Siegfried Ruhemann and the Discovery of Ninhydrin, *J. Chem. Educ.*, **42**, 386.

ZACHARIUS, R. M., AND E. A. TALLEY, (1962), Elution Behavior of Naturally Occurring Ninhydrin-Positive Compounds during Ion Exchange Chromatography, *Anal. Chem.*, **34**, 1551.

6

THE DETERMINATION OF N-TERMINAL
RESIDUES AND SEQUENCES

Until 1945 when Sanger (1945) devised his DNP method, there was no satisfactory way of deciding whether all possible peptide bonds had formed in a protein and the chain, therefore, was cyclic or whether one or more chains were present with the anticipated amino group at one end and the carboxyl group at the other. At the present time a study of the N-terminal residues is almost a traditional beginning for the determination of sequence. If the N-terminal residue(s) has been identified, it serves as a starting point for laying out the entire final sequence—some fragment of the molecule must have an identical N-terminal residue. As was pointed out in Chapter 4, a determination of the N-terminal residues serves as an excellent indicator of homogeneity.

It must be recognized that currently satisfactory methods for free α-amino groups show only the minimum number of N-terminal residues and, hence, of polypeptide chains. In some proteins, the N-terminal amino group is not free but has been "blocked" or, in other words, has attached to it some group that alters its chemical characteristics. Indeed both free and blocked N-terminal amino groups may be present. Despite these limitations, an investigation of the N-terminal residues of a protein (and of any peptides that may be isolated from it in the study of the entire sequence) is likely to give much valuable information.

SANGER'S METHOD—THE DNP PROCEDURE

Any N-terminal method attempts to attach to the N-terminal amino acid, at least for a time, some group that will identify it in the presence of all other amino acids after complete hydrolysis or that, by further reaction, will remove the N-terminal amino acid without altering the remainder of the chain. The DNP method (Sanger, 1945) achieves this goal by forming a nitrogen-carbon bond that is stable during the acid hydrolysis of peptide bonds. The reactions for this method are outlined in Reaction Scheme 4.

Reaction Scheme 4.

DNFB[1] in alkaline solution reacts with the amino group of the peptide or protein to form the DNP derivative. Many modifications of this step have been described, but it is vital that a basic pH be maintained because reaction I occurs only with the unprotonated amino group. Basic conditions are normally maintained with sodium carbonate, with an easily volatilized amine such as trimethylamine, or with a pH-stat[2] in aqueous or aqueous-alcoholic medium at temperatures between room temperature and 40°C for several hours with an excess of DNFB. Despite the slight solubility of DNFB in water, a most effective set of conditions is an entirely aqueous medium at 40°C that is vigorously shaken or stirred. At the end of the reaction, acidification of the reaction mixture usually results in precipitation of the protein if it has not already precipitated during the reaction. If an aqueous-alcoholic medium is used, the protein may be insoluble even before the

[1] Defined in Chapter 2.
[2] A pH-stat maintains a constant pH by addition of acid or base (in this instance) depending upon the reaction that is occurring.

reaction, which then occurs in a two-phase system. The DNP-protein after filtration or centrifugation must be thoroughly washed with acidified water to remove salts (such as sodium fluoride from the reaction) and then with ethanol and ethyl ether to remove 2,4-dinitrophenol, which is formed from the hydrolysis of some DNFB. After peptides have been dinitrophenylated, they often may be extracted from the acidified reaction mixture with ether or ethyl acetate, because they are no longer dipolarionic. Extraction usually is feasible only with nonbasic DNP-peptides about the size of pentapeptides or less. Because DNP compounds are yellow, their progress in the extraction is easily followed.

In the next stage of the procedure, a known weight of dry DNP-protein is hydrolyzed in refluxing $6N$ hydrochloric acid (reaction II). The time of hydrolysis is determined by considerations that will be discussed below. With the exception of DNP-arginine and di-DNP-histidine, the DNP-amino acids may be extracted from the hydrolyzate, identified qualitatively, and determined quantitatively.

A variety of chromatographic methods that use paper, thin layer, or column procedures is available for the identification and determination of DNP-amino acids. Paper methods (reviewed by Biserte et al., 1959) usually require rather large correction factors in quantitative determinations, perhaps because it has not always been appreciated that DNP-amino acids are photosensitive in alkaline medium to natural diffuse day light (not direct sunlight) although not to artificial light whether incandescent or fluorescent. Column chromatographic methods for DNP-amino acids usually use silicic acid (Green and Kay, 1952) as a support under a variety of conditions and have even been automated (Kesner et al., 1963). Quantitative determination is easily made spectrophotometrically in sodium bicarbonate or glacial acetic acid. In the latter solvent, the DNP-amino acids have an absorption maximum at 340 mμ that is characteristic of all DNP-amino acids (or DNP-peptides). DNP-Proline and DNP-hydroxyproline have an altered spectrum because they are DNP-imino acids.

Although the DNP method is meant to be quantitative, it is well to consider certain factors that may make it less than quantitative (Rhinesmith et al., 1957).

If the initial reaction with DNFB is not quantitative, the method cannot be. The experimental evidence suggests that the reaction is essentially quantitative, because relatively short as well as long dinitrophenylations give identical results. It must be realized that not only α-amino groups but other groups as well react with DNFB. The ε-amino group of lysine, the imidazole group of histidine, the hydroxyl group of tyrosine, and the sulfhydryl group of cysteine will be dinitrophenylated but not, for example, the hydroxyl group of serine or threonine. The reaction of those groups does not interfere with the determination of the N-terminal residues, but because they are usually present in far greater number than the N-terminal residues, an adequate excess of DNFB must be added.

Hydrolytic release of the N-terminal amino acid must also be complete. The considerations that have been discussed in Chapter 5 about hydrolysis pertain equally here. In short peptides at least, all DNP-amino acids except DNP-valine are quantitatively released in 4 hr in refluxing 6N hydrochloric acid. The main problem during hydrolysis is not the release of the DNP-amino acid as such but the partial or complete destruction of the bond between the DNP group and the amino nitrogen. There is more or less partial destruction of all DNP-amino acids during 24 hr in refluxing 6N acid, but DNP-proline, DNP-hydroxyproline, and DNP-glycine are completely destroyed. Disregard of such facts and the routine use of this period of hydrolysis has led some authors to overlook N-terminal glycyl residues. It is important that times of hydrolysis should be varied greatly and especially that some should be short—15 to 60 min. Correction for hydrolytic destruction is usually made by determining the loss of DNP-amino acid under the same conditions; this method admittedly can not correct for any loss that occurred before or during the hydrolytic cleavage.

Before a final calculation of the number of N-terminal residues can be made, the effective molecular weight of the DNP-protein must be known. Because many groups other than the N-terminal amino groups react with DNFB, the molecular weight of the DNP-protein will be considerably more than that of the free protein. The equivalence between free and DNP-protein can best be assessed by an amino acid analysis of a known weight of DNP-protein. If, for example, the weight content of those amino acids, such as aspartic acid, proline, and glycine, which would not normally react with DNFB (except if N-terminal) is only three-fourths that of the free protein, the effective molecular weight of the DNP-protein for this calculation is four-thirds that of the free protein.

When carefully applied, the DNP method has been and continues to be an excellent procedure for N-terminal amino acids. Representative results are given in Table 6. The examples are those for which the results can now be compared with the complete sequence. The data in parentheses for the hemoglobins are the results of later redeterminations before the sequence was known. On the whole, the determinations agree well with the presently known N-terminal results. Actually, these results from the DNP method served well in the final determination of the complete sequence.

TABLE 6. *N-Terminal Residues of Some Proteins as Determined by the DNP Method*

Protein	Assumed mol wt	N-Terminal residues	Number per assumed mol wt	From the sequence
Carboxypeptidase	34,000	Asparagine	1	
α-Chymotrypsin	21,500	Alanine	1	1
		Leucine	1	
		Isoleucine		1
		½ Cystine		1
Hemoglobins				
Bovine	66,000	Valine	2(2)	2
		Methionine	2(2)	2
Horse	66,000	Valine	6(3.7)	4
Human adult	66,000	Valine	5(3.6)	4
Human fetal	66,000	Valine	2–3(2)	2
		Glycine	(2)	2
Insulin	12,000	Phenylalanine	2	2
(Ox, pig, sheep)		Glycine	2	2
Lysozyme	14,000	Lysine	1	1
Myoglobin (whale)	17,000	Valine	1	1
Papain	20,000	Isoleucine	1	1
Ribonuclease	?	Lysine	1	1

The DNP method can also be used to identify short sequences near the N terminus. DNP-peptides frequently can be isolated after hydrolysis for some minutes at refluxing temperature or for some days at 37°C in 6*N* hydrochloric acid. Thus, when DNP-lysozyme was refluxed for only 10 min in 6*N* hydrochloric acid (Schroeder, 1952), the following DNP compounds elucidated the sequence of four residues:

di-DNP-Lysine
di-DNP-Lys-Val
di-DNP-Lys-Val-Phe
di-DNP-Lys-Val-Phe-Gly.

The relative proportion even gave some idea of the strength of the various bonds toward acidic hydrolysis. In much the same way, human hemoglobin A was found to have pairs of chains with the sequences Val-Leu and Val-His-Leu (Rhinesmith *et al.*, 1957a). Usually, sequences determined in this way are relatively short because some especially labile bond is hydrolyzed. This is the case with hemoglobin A where the sequences are Val-Leu-Ser- and Val-His-Leu-Thr-, because peptide bonds associated with the amino group of serine and threonine are exceedingly susceptible to acid hydrolysis.

Before the advent of automatic amino acid analyzers, some use was made of the DNP method for amino acid analysis. After acidic hydrolysis, the amino acids were dinitrophenylated, separated, and quantitatively estimated. This method is excellent for small peptides and has been applied with some success to proteins.

EDMAN'S METHOD—THE PTH PROCEDURE

Although short sequences near the N terminus may frequently be identified by the DNP method, it is designed to determine the sequence of a single amino acid—the N-terminal. Edman's method or the PTH procedure,[3] on the other hand, under the best conditions is a method of sequence determination and removes one residue at a time sequentially from the N terminus (Edman, 1950).

The procedure follows the series of reactions in Reaction Scheme 5. The initial coupling (reaction I) of phenylisothiocyanate with the N-terminal amino group is made in alkaline medium at about pH 9 for several hours. Either the reaction is carried out in solution, or the peptide or protein is applied to a paper strip, which is then saturated with phenylisothiocyanate and suspended in an atmosphere of basic reagents during the reaction. After the excess reagents have been extracted, the PTC derivative is degraded under acidic conditions (reaction II). This degradation is not a hydrolysis for it may be carried out in an anhydrous medium. Under these conditions, the intermediate thiazolinone may be isolated. The thiazolinone in aqueous acid rearranges (reaction III) to the phenylthiohydantoin or PTH-amino acid.

The PTH-amino acids commonly are identified by paper chromatographic methods. They are easily detected as white spots on a purple background by spraying a starched paper with an iodine-azide reagent. Quantitative methods by both column and paper chromatography have been devised. A popular qualitative and quantitative method is a "subtractive" one that is applicable to relatively short peptides. For instance, after the N-terminal residue has been removed from a peptide of known amino acid composition, the remaining peptide (minus now the N-terminal amino acid) is again analyzed. The type of amino acid that has decreased in amount is the N-terminal one.

The great virtue of the Edman method lies in the possibility of

---

[3] Defined in Chapter 2.

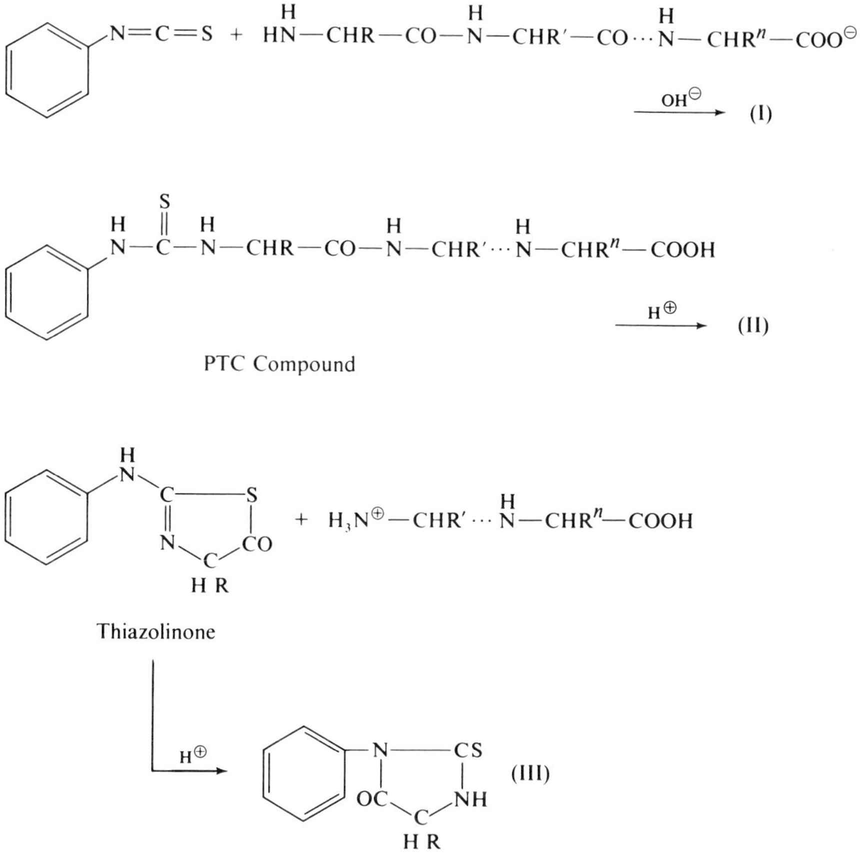

$$\text{(I)} \quad \xrightarrow{\text{OH}^{\ominus}}$$

PTC Compound

$$\text{(II)} \quad \xrightarrow{\text{H}^{\oplus}}$$

Thiazolinone

$$\text{(III)} \quad \xleftarrow{\text{H}^{\oplus}}$$

PTH-Amino acid

Reaction Scheme 5.

sequential degradation because at the conclusion of the reactions the original protein or peptide has one less residue and is ready for further degradation. It has had its greatest application to sequence determination in peptides and will be discussed further in this regard in Chapter 11. The method has been applied with less success to proteins and, in general, has not given as quantitative results as the Sanger method. It seems as though a new era in the application of the Edman method to proteins is about to begin. Edman and Begg (1967) have published the details of a "protein sequenator." This automatic apparatus carries out about 15 cycles of degradation in 24 hr. Further comment is made in Chapter 8 (p. 90).

We need not stress that such factors as quantitativeness of the reaction, that have been discussed for the DNP method apply equally here.

THE CYANATE METHOD

The cyanate method of Stark and Smyth (1963) in principle is that of the Edman procedure except that it is not designed to be a degradative one. In it, the hydantoin rather than the phenylthiohydantoin is formed, isolated, degraded to the amino acid, and determined as such (Reaction Scheme 6).

$$NCO^{\ominus} + \overset{H}{\underset{H}{HN^{\oplus}}}-CHR-CO-\overset{H}{N}-CHR'-CO \cdots \overset{H}{N}-CHR''-COO^{\ominus} \xrightarrow{\text{pH 8}}$$

$$\overset{H}{HN}-CO-\overset{H}{N}-CHR-CO-\overset{H}{N}-CHR'-CO \cdots \overset{H}{N}-CHR''-COOH \xrightarrow{H^{\oplus}}$$

$$\underset{\underset{CO}{\diagdown \diagup}}{\overset{CHR-CO}{\underset{HN \qquad NH}{|\qquad\qquad|}}} + \overset{H}{\underset{H}{HN^{\oplus}}}-CHR'-CO \cdots \overset{H}{N}-CHR''-COOH$$

Hydrolysis

$$\longrightarrow H_2N-CHR-COOH + NH_3 + CO_2$$

Reaction Scheme 6.

The reaction with cyanate to produce the carbamyl derivative is done at basic pH in $8M$ urea in order to denature the protein. After isolation of the carbamylated protein by precipitation or dialysis, the hydantoin is then released with $6N$ acid at 100°C for an hour. Ion-exchange chromatography is used to separate the hydantoin from free amino acids and peptides. Hydrolysis of the hydantoin to the free amino acid either by alkaline or acidic medium is finally followed by quantitative determination with the automatic amino acid analyzer. In view of the sensitivity of procedures of amino acid analysis, the method is potentially applicable to rather small samples. The originators have used less than 0.2 μmole successfully.

As in the DNP and PTH methods, such features as quantitative reaction at any step, destruction of the derivative at any step, and the like come into consideration. Special modification is necessary when certain amino acids are N termini, and blanks are required to correct for the presence of extraneous amino acids that do not derive from the N termini.

The procedure is relatively new and has had little application yet. In tests with peptides and proteins with known N-terminal residues, the yields have been 85 to 95 percent of the expected.

THE DANSYL METHOD

A recent development that basically parallels the DNP method is the "dansyl" method so-called from the abbreviation for the reagent which is 1-dimethylaminonaphthalene-5-sulfonyl chloride[4] (dansyl chloride or DNS-Cl) (Gray, 1967). The product (Reaction Scheme 7) contains a sulfur-nitrogen bond which is as stable to hydrolysis as the

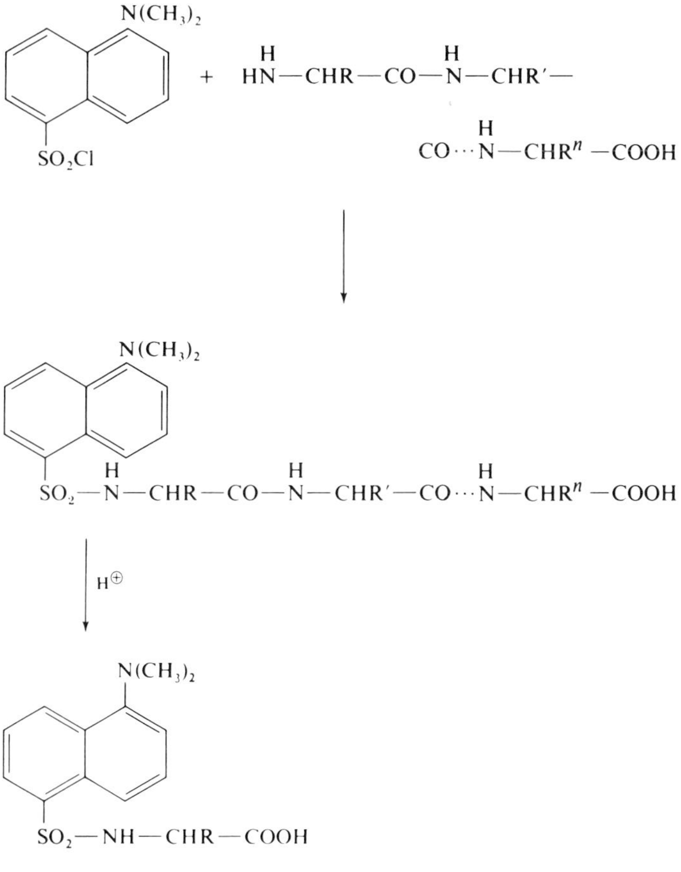

Reaction Scheme 7.

---

[4] Defined in Chapter 2.

carbon-nitrogen bond of the DNP derivatives. The DNS-amino acid may be identified by paper electrophoresis or by paper or thin-layer chromatography.

The potential advantage of the method lies in the fact that the DNS-amino acids are strongly fluorescent when irradiated with the proper wavelength of ultraviolet light. It is reported that as little as 0.01 nanomole per spot may be detected visually but that 0.1 nanomole is the practical lower limit. The method, therefore, offers a means of determining N-terminal residues for those workers who by choice or necessity desire to work with minute amounts of material.

This procedure is more effective with peptides than with proteins and is designed more as a qualitative than as a quantitative method. Like other methods, it succeeds only with careful attention to detail and like other methods, it has problems unique to it alone. For example, DNS-peptides with valine or leucine as the N-terminal amino acid hydrolyze to free DNS-valine or DNS-leucine with difficulty under standard hydrolytic conditions. Unless this fact is realized, a false interpretation of the results may well be made. In combination with the Edman procedure, it may be used in sequence determination (Chapter 11, p. 143).

THE DETERMINATION OF BLOCKING GROUPS

When some of the above described methods were first applied to proteins, examples were quickly forthcoming of proteins that apparently contain no or at most fractional N-terminal residues. Fractional residues may, of course, simply be indicative of impurity, but the absence of any N-terminal residue, at first, was interpreted as due to unreactivity because of inaccessibility or steric hindrance or as due to the actual absence of N- and C-terminal residues because the protein was cyclic. Occasionally a C-terminal residue could be detected and another form of protein such as

was suggested. As more sophisticated methods of investigation were developed, it became clear that failure to yield a derivative to the common N-terminal reagents was caused by a blocking or masking of the N-terminal amino group by some group that altered the chemical behavior. The first to be discovered and still most commonly observed blocking group is the acetyl group. It was detected originally in tobacco mosaic virus protein by Narita (1958) and has since been found in cytochrome *c* and in other proteins. The formyl group is present in the small peptide antibiotic known as valine-gramicidin A (Sarges and Witkop, 1965). An unusual group has been detected in a minor hemoglobin component of normal blood; its structure, still incompletely elucidated, is known to involve the linkage of an aldehyde or ketone to the N-terminal amino group in a Schiff's base type of linkage— R=N-Val-His-Leu-etc. (Holmquist and Schroeder, 1966). Wilkinson *et. al.* (1966) have detected pyrrolidone carboxylic acid, which has the structure

$$
\begin{array}{c}
H_2C{-\!\!-\!\!-}CH_2 \\
\mid \qquad\qquad \mid \\
C \qquad\quad CH{-}COOH \\
\diagup\!\!\diagdown \quad \diagup \\
O \qquad N \\
\mid \\
H
\end{array}
$$

as the N-terminal amino acid of the heavy chain of a rabbit immunoglobulin. This is "blocking" by cyclization. Just as glutamine in acid solution cyclizes to pyrrolidone carboxylic acid, so peptides N-terminal in a glutaminyl residue will usually be found to have cyclized if they have been exposed to acid.

If the usual N-terminal methods fail to detect a free amino group, it is natural to look for the common acetyl group. It has been identified as the hydrazide or as methyl acetate after reaction with methanolic HCl. The volatility of methyl acetate makes for ready identification and determination by gas chromatography. It can hardly be said, however, that a general method is available for identifying possible blocking groups. Although the acetyl group can be detected with relative ease, much chemical detective work was required in the above example where the blocking group was an aldehyde or ketone. In all probability, blocking groups of quite different character remain to be detected.

The presence of a blocking group, in general, makes it difficult to determine the number of chains in a molecule and is an effective obstacle to the application of a degradative method such as the Edman procedure.

REFERENCES

BISERTE, G., J. W. HOLLEMAN, J. HOLLEMAN-DEHOVE, AND P. SAUTIERE (1959), Chromatographie sur Papier des Dinitrophenylaminoacides, *J. Chromatog.*, **2**, 225.

EDMAN, P. (1950), Method for Determination of the Amino Acid Sequence in Peptides, *Acta Chem. Scand.*, **4**, 283.

EDMAN, P., AND G. BEGG (1967), A Protein Sequenator, *European J. Biochem.*, **1**, 80.

GRAY, W. R. (1967), Dansyl Chloride Procedure, in *Enzyme Structure* (Vol. 11 of *Methods in Enzymology*), C. H. W. Hirs, ed., New York, Academic Press, p. 139.

GREEN, F. C., AND L. M. KAY (1952), Separation of Sixteen Dinitrophenylamino Acids by Adsorption Chromatography on Silicic Acid-Celite, *Anal. Chem.* **24**, 726.

HOLMQUIST, W. R., AND W. A. SCHROEDER (1966), A New N-Terminal Blocking Group Involving a Schiff Base in Hemoglobin A_{Ic}, *Biochemistry*, **5**, 2489.

KESNER, L., E. MUNTWYLER, G. E. GRIFFIN, AND J. ABRAMS (1963), Automatic Column Chromatography of Ether and Water-Soluble 2,4-Dinitrophenyl-Derivatives of Amino Acids, Peptides, and Amines, *Anal. Chem.*, **35**, 83.

NARITA, K. (1958), Isolation of Acetylpeptide from Enzymic Digests of TMV-Protein, *Biochim. Biophys. Acta*, **28**, 184.

RHINESMITH, H. S., W. A. SCHROEDER, AND L. PAULING (1957), The N-Terminal Amino Acid Residues of Normal Adult Human Hemoglobin: A Quantitative Study of Certain Aspects of Sanger's DNP-Method, *J. Am. Chem. Soc.*, **79**, 609.

RHINESMITH, H. S., W. A. SCHROEDER, AND L. PAULING (1957a), A Quantitative Study of the Hydrolysis of Human Dinitrophenyl (DNP) globin: The Number and Kind of Polypeptide Chains in Normal Adult Human Hemoglobin, *J. Am. Chem. Soc.*, **79**, 4682.

SANGER, F. (1945), The Free Amino Groups of Insulin, *Biochem. J.*, **39**, 507.

SARGES, R., AND B. WITKOP (1965), Gramicidin A. V. The Structure of Valine- and Isoleucine-gramicidin A, *J. Am. Chem. Soc.*, **87**, 2011.

SCHROEDER, W. A. (1952), Sequence of Four Amino Acids at the Amino End of the Single Polypeptide Chain of Lysozyme, *J. Am. Chem. Soc.*, **74**, 5118.

STARK, G. R., AND D. G. SMYTH (1963), The Use of Cyanate for the Determination of NH_2-terminal Residues in Proteins, *J. Biol. Chem.*, **238**, 214.

WILKINSON, J. M., E. M. PRESS, AND R. R. PORTER (1966), The N-Terminal Sequence of the Heavy Chain of Rabbit Immunoglobulin IgG, *Biochem. J.*, **100**, 303.

7

THE DETERMINATION OF C-TERMINAL
RESIDUES AND SEQUENCES

The obvious utility of a knowledge of N-terminal residues as we have discussed it in the preceding chapter applies equally well to C-terminal residues. Equality of the two numbers makes blocking groups unlikely. Unfortunately, in few instances has this ideal situation been reached. It should be mentioned here that the peptide antibiotic valine-gramicidin A that was mentioned in the last chapter is blocked not only in the N-terminal but also in the C-terminal position; the C-terminal carboxyl group has reacted with the amino group of ethanolamine. Although the N-terminal procedures are among the best and most useful methods that have been applied in sequence determinations, methods for the identification of C-terminal residues have been of limited usefulness. The chemical behavior of the carboxyl group is so different from that of the amino group that derivatives stable to hydrolysis have not been successfully made. Although chemical reactions such as the reduction of the esterified carboxyl group to the amino alcohol and its subsequent identification have been studied extensively (Chibnall and Rees, 1958), side reactions have tended to limit their usefulness and to invalidate results. Only two methods, a chemical and an enzymatic one, have been applied to any extent, and neither of these forms a derivative of the C-terminal residue. The effectiveness of an entirely new approach that has recently been suggested remains to be determined.

THE HYDRAZINOLYTIC METHOD

The principle of the hydrazinolytic method of Akabori and collaborators (1956) is simple. Just as hydrolysis adds water across each peptide bond to produce free amino acids, so hydrazinolysis would be expected to produce hydrazides of all amino acids except the C-terminal as indicated in Reaction Scheme 8. Only the C-terminal amino acid will produce a free amino acid because a carboxyl group does not react with hydrazine to give the hydrazide. In a hydrazinolyzate the C-terminal amino acid will be unique among the products.

$$\overset{N}{HN}-CHR-\overset{H}{CO}\cdots\overset{H}{N}-CHR'-CO-\overset{H}{N}-CHR''-COOH + N_2H_4 \longrightarrow$$

$$\overset{H}{HN}-CHR-CONHNH_2 + \cdots + \overset{H}{HN}-CHR'-CONHNH_2 + \overset{H}{HN}-CHR''-COOH$$

Reaction Scheme 8.

In most applications, the protein has been heated with excess anhydrous hydrazine for about 10 hr at 100°C. The exact conditions must be determined by trial with the individual protein. Hydrazine sulfate has been used as a catalyst to reduce the temperature of hydrazinolysis and hopefully thus to minimize destructive effects. After the appropriate reaction time, excess hydrazine is removed by volatilization.

Isolation, identification, and estimation of the C-terminal amino acid has commonly been made in one of two ways. In the first, the entire reaction mixture is dinitrophenylated, and by an involved extractive procedure, the C-terminal DNP-amino acid is isolated. The extraction is based largely on the fact that the DNP-amino acid as the anion in basic solution is not extracted by organic solvents whereas the di-DNP-hydrazides are. It will be apparent that a non-C-terminal glutamyl or aspartyl residue will also behave as an anion; this fact must be taken into consideration in evaluating the experiment. The DNP-amino acid can than be studied by methods that we have described in Chapter 6. A second type of procedure removes the hydrazides by reaction with an aldehyde. The Schiff's bases formed when the reaction mixture in water is treated with benzaldehyde, isovaleraldehyde, or other aldehyde can be separated by filtration if the products are insoluble or by separation of the phases if the products remain in solution in excess reagent. Quantitative estimation then can proceed directly or through the DNP-amino acid.

The above methods were devised before chromatographic procedures on ion-exchange resins were in common use for amino acids. The C-terminal amino acid can be isolated easily from the hydrazinolyzate by chromatography on a column of a strong cation-exchange resin with volatile developers; the basic hydrazides are strongly fixed, and the free amino acids are rapidly eluted (Braun and Schroeder, 1967). After the volatile solvents have been removed, the amino acid(s) can be qualitatively and quantitatively determined by automatic amino acid analysis. If modern methods are applied, the quantitative determination of the free C-terminal amino acid in the reaction mixture should be the least difficult part of the procedure.

The greatest problem lies in the fact that the apparently simple chemistry of the reaction does not seem to be easily realized in practice. Although occasional good yields have been reported, in general, they are likely to be less than 60 percent of the theoretical. Hydrazine sulfate as a catalyst seems to be of uncertain value, but hydrazinolysis in the presence of Amberlite IRC-50 has given almost theoretical yields with several test proteins (Braun and Schroeder, 1967). The mixture of protein, hydrazine, and Amberlite IRC-50 was heated at 80°C for periods of 10 to 100 hr depending upon the protein. The separation and estimation were made chromatographically as mentioned above. Of the eleven proteins that were tested by the method, five gave results that were 90 to 100 percent of the theoretical and most of the others gave results above 70 percent. The latter results could perhaps have been improved by some modification of conditions. In no instance were extraneous amino acids present in more than a few percent. Although negative results might be obtained in other applications, false positive results seem unlikely. The method is unsatisfactory for arginine which is known to be altered and destroyed and for asparagine and glutamine.

When older methods of hydrazinolysis have been used, the record of successes that have been substantiated by complete determination of sequence has not been impressive. As an example, lysozyme was shown first by carboxypeptidase (see below) and then by hydrazinolysis to have C-terminal leucine as indeed the complete sequence shows (Chapter 14). Actually, lysozyme is a fairly small protein and prior to its examination by hydrazinolysis had been rather convincingly shown to have a single chain by N-terminal determination and other evidence.

By partial hydrazinolysis (that is, by incomplete reaction so that some peptide bonds are unbroken) of tobacco mosaic virus protein, a peptide from the C terminus was isolated and the sequence of a few residues near the C terminus was established, but a similar application to lysozyme has subsequently been shown to have given an incorrect result.

THE CARBOXYPEPTIDASE METHOD

The only other C-terminal method that has enjoyed reasonable success is an enzymatic one. In fact, it was used about 1930 by

Grassmann *et al.* (1930) in the determination of the structure of glutathione, which is

$$\underset{\underset{NH_2}{|}}{HOOC-CH}-CH_2-CH_2-CO-\overset{H}{N}-\underset{\underset{CH_2-SH}{|}}{CH}-CO-\overset{H}{N}-CH_2-COOH.$$

Carboxypeptidases act on proteins or peptides to release the amino acid which has a free α-carboxyl group. Two carboxypeptidases, A and B, are now recognized. The former, the less specific of the two, will not release lysyl, arginyl, or prolyl residues, and glutamic or aspartic acid may block its action although conflicting reports about the latter two are to be found. On the other hand, carboxypeptidase B will remove only lysyl, arginyl, or ornithyl residues.

Both enzymes are isolated from bovine pancreas as zymogens that must be activated by trypsin. Complete removal of proteolytic enzymes from the carboxypeptidases may be difficult and may introduce complications into the use of the method because proteolytic action will present residues to be cleaved by the carboxypeptidase. The action of proteolytic enzymes can be prevented by inactivating them. The carboxypeptidases are active at approximately pH 7–8.

The successful application of carboxypeptidase requires that the release of amino acid be studied kinetically. It is apparent that, if carboxypeptidase releases an amino acid, another immediately becomes available for cleavage—and so on. In an early stage of the reaction, the concentration of substance from which one or more residues has been cleaved will be small, and the initial rate of release of the second and following residues may be expected to be slow. An ideal example is the action of the enzyme on corticotropin (White, 1953) as presented in Fig. 15. The release of phenylalanine took place quickly and then ceased. After much phenylalanine had been freed, both glutamic acid and leucine began to appear in free form at distinctly different rates. This experiment was done under typical conditions at pH 7.5 and 37°C. After samples had been removed at appropriate times, and the reaction had been stopped by acidification, the reaction mixture was examined qualitatively and quantitatively for free amino acids. In the application of this method, the identification and estimation presents no problem because the remaining protein can usually be precipitated by trichloracetic acid, and the solution can be examined directly by the analytical method of choice.

Another example of a brilliantly successful experiment with carboxypeptidase is its application to tobacco mosaic virus (TMV). The

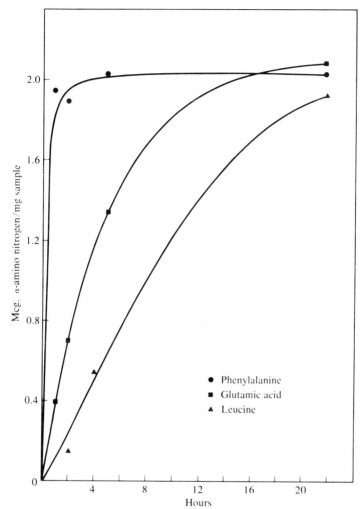

Figure 15. Rate of liberation of amino acids from corticotropin-A by treatment with carboxypeptidase. [Source: White, *J. Am. Chem. Soc.*, **75**, 4877 (1953). Copyright 1953 by the American Chemical Society. Reprinted by permission of the copyright owner.]

protein of this virus released threonine and only threonine in sufficient quantity to lead to the conclusion that about 3,000 C-terminal residues were present (Harris and Knight, 1955). Indeed, it is now known that TMV contains about 3,000 subunits of 158 residues or about 17,500 molecular weight each; this C-terminal determination was one of the first steps in the elucidation of the structure of TMV protein.

Unfortunately, such straightforward applications are rare, because the nature of the residue plays an important role in determining the rate at which it is released. Incorrect conclusions have been reached because the release of the first residue was the rate limiting step. When such is the case, the first two residues appear in equal quantity as a function of time. The conclusion that two chains are present is incorrect, because the two residues have been successively released.

The method presents sufficient ambiguities and problems that the results of its application must be regarded with caution. Success in the above two examples may be mainly a result of the fact that further reaction was blocked by proline; in corticotropin the sequence is -Pro-Leu-Glu-Phe, and in TMV protein it is -Pro-Ala-Thr.

The carboxypeptidases have been applied to small peptides with more success (Chapter 11).

Reaction Scheme 9.

THE RACEMIZATION METHOD

A new approach to the problem of the identification of C-terminal residues has been devised by a group of Japanese workers (Matsuo *et al.*, 1966). The procedure involves the racemization of the C-terminal residue and the concurrent selective labelling of that residue with tritium. The reaction is believed to occur by the course depicted in Reaction Scheme 9.

The first reaction in the presence of acetic anhydride results in acetylation and in oxazolone formation between the C-terminal and the adjacent residue. Under the influence of alkaline conditions, the hydrogen ion is removed from the α-carbon atom of the C-terminal amino acid and the indicated equilibrium is set up. Hydrolysis of the oxazolone in the presence of tritium oxide introduces the tritium label on the α-carbon atom. After complete acid hydrolysis, the amino acid in which radioactivity is detected must derive from the C-terminal residue. The authors have applied the method successfully to insulin, the hormone angiotensin, and to several synthetic peptides.

The concept is a new one whose worth remains to be tested.

REFERENCES

AKABORI, S., K. OHNO, T. IKENAKA, Y. OKADA, H. HANAFUSA, I. HARUNA, A. TSUGITA, K. SUGAE, AND T. MATSUSHIMA (1956), Hydrazinolysis of Peptides and Proteins. II. Fundamental Studies on the Determination of the Carboxyl-ends of Proteins, *Bull. Chem. Soc. Japan*, **29**, 507.

BRAUN, V., AND W. A. SCHROEDER (1967), A Reinvestigation of the Hydrazinolytic Procedure for the Determination of C-Terminal Amino Acids, *Arch. Biochem. Biophys.*, **118**, 241.

CHIBNALL, A. C., AND M. W. REES (1958), Studies on the Amide and C-Terminal Residues in Proteins. 1. The Characterization of the C-Terminal Residue, *Biochem. J.*, **68**, 105.

GRASSMANN, W., H. DYCKERHOFF, AND H. EIBELER (1930), Über die enzymatisch Spaltung des Glutathions. I., *Z. physiol. Chem.*, **189**, 112.

HARRIS, J. I., AND C. A. KNIGHT (1955), Studies on the Action of Carboxypeptidase on Tobacco Mosaic Virus, *J. Biol. Chem.*, **214**, 215.

MATSUO, H., Y. FUJIMOTO, AND T. TATSUNO (1966), A Novel Method for the Determination of C-Terminal Amino Acid in Polypeptides by Selective Tritium Labelling, *Biochem. Biophys. Res. Commun.*, **22**, 69.

WHITE, W. F. (1953), Studies on Pituitary Adrenocorticotropin VII. A C-Terminal Sequence of Corticotropin-A, *J. Am. Chem. Soc.*, **75**, 4877.

8

THE STRATEGY OF SEQUENCE DETERMINATION

The determination of the amino acid composition of a protein as well as a successful examination of the N- and C-terminal residues will do much to answer some of the questions that have been posed in Chapter 4. These answers will probably show the investigator that his particular protein has its own individual features. This information will no doubt make it apparent that a further investigation of structure and a determination of the sequence will be beset by various problems whether they be mere size or some special feature not yet observed in other proteins. This uniqueness of the individual protein removes the determination of sequence from the routine and places obstacles in the path to final success. Despite problems, some obvious and some less apparent, available methods now permit many data to be assembled with speed if not without great effort. Much progress has been made since Sanger and collaborators first placed the amino acids of insulin in sequence. It in no way detracts from their accomplishments to point out that the A chain of insulin with 21 residues and the B chain with 30 residues are likely to be shorter than some *peptides* in partial hydrolyzates of most proteins. Experience has shown that the time and effort that are required to complete the last 10 percent of a sequence may be several times as great as that required to complete the first 90 percent.

When a knowledge of amino acid composition and of N- and C-terminal residues has been gained (or even sometimes without some of this information), the initial steps toward a complete sequence are straightforward and yet they are relatively circumscribed. In this chapter, we shall describe the approaches to the problem of sequence determination and the way in which these approaches are applied.

 Reference for Chapter 8, p. 92.

SEQUENCE DETERMINATION BY REPEATED DEGRADATION

The Fischer–Hofmeister idea of the polypeptide chain makes the linkage of all amino acid residues identical. The most intriguing way of determining sequence is to remove each of these identically linked residues one by one from one end or the other and to identify each residue after it has been removed. Modern methods for the identification and quantitative estimation of an amino acid whether free or as a derivative are so well developed that the identification of any amino acid so freed poses no special problem. The crux of the matter lies in the removal of one residue after another under such mild conditions

TABLE 7.   *Yield of Amino Acid Derivative after Some Steps of Sequential Degradation Assuming Certain Yields at Each Step*

Number of steps	Yield per step		
	99 percent	*95 percent*	*90 percent*
10	90 percent	60 percent	35 percent
50	60 percent	8 percent	0.5 percent
100	36 percent	0.6 percent	0.003 percent
Amt. of starting material[a]	0.3 μmole	17 μmoles	3500 μmoles

[a] For 100 degradations, if a minimum of 0.1 μmole of amino acid or derivative is needed for identification.

that a peptide bond is split only when its place in the succession has been reached. The sole method yet devised that potentially is able to degrade sequentially is the Edman procedure (Chapter 6, p. 74). If a method is to be equal to the task of sequential degradation, what requirements must it meet? As we shall see in Chapter 14 (p. 170) where the results of the determination of sequence are presented, polypeptide chains frequently are 100 to 300 residues in length. Consequently, a procedure that could degrade sequentially for 100 residues would be of great use. One might hope to be able to cleave longer chains into parts of this length, to separate the parts, and to apply the procedure to each part. If a sequential procedure is to be successful over a large number of degradations, the yield must be excellent at each degradation. Table 7 examines this requirement. The headings of columns 2, 3, and 4 assume a certain percentage yield at each step. The numbers under these headings give the yield after the designated number of steps in terms of the percentage of the yield on the first step of the sequential degradation.

At a yield per degradation of 99 percent, the 100th degraded residue would be obtained in about $\frac{1}{3}$ the amount of the first residue. If the procedure for identifying the degraded residue requires 0.1 μmole, 0.3 μmole of protein at the start of the degradation would yield this amount after 100 degradations. A 0.3-μmole sample is only 4–5 mg for a 100- to 150-residue chain. However, a yield of 99 percent is exceptional for an organic reaction, and even if we assume the excellent yield of 90 percent it is evident that only 10 degradations would require starting material equal to that for 100 degradations at 99 percent yield. With a 90-percent yield, the amount of starting material for 100 degradations is unthinkable. Because sensitive methods of determining and detecting amino acids or their derivatives are now available, the requirement that at least 0.1 μmole be available after a degradation is perhaps unrealistic. Thus, 0.00001 μmole (0.01 nanomole) is detectable by the dansyl method (Chapter 6, p. 78), and 0.1 nanomole is a satisfactory working amount. However, if for practical purposes we require 1 nanomole (0.001 μmole) from any degradation, 100 degradations with 90 percent yield would still require 35 μmoles of starting material.

Although the above considerations may seem to be idealistic, they appear to have been realized as a result of the long and intensive investigation of Edman. Edman and Begg (1967) have now described a "protein sequenator," a machine that automatically subjects a protein to the Edman degradation. Basically, the protein sequenator introduces and removes reagents from a spinning cup upon the sides of which the protein has been precipitated. One cycle of reaction to remove a single residue requires about 1.5 hr. At this point, the amino acid is in the form of the thiazolinone (p. 74) and is automatically removed from the machine into a fraction collector. Each residue so collected is then converted to the PTH-amino acid and identified. The results of the application of this procedure to hump back whale myoglobin yielded the sequence of 60 residues. A sample of only 0.25 μmole was necessary, because the average yield was 98 per cent. The results are truly excellent.

What will be the impact of this machine upon methods of sequence determination remains to be seen. It in no way detracts from the excellent work of these investigators to point out that the procedure is inapplicable to some proteins—for example, if a blocking group is present.

SEQUENCE DETERMINATION BY DISSIMILAR PARTIAL CLEAVAGE AND OVERLAPPING OF SEQUENCES

Despite greatly improved methodology and increased ease of investigation, the basic principle used to determine amino acid sequence has not altered much since Sanger determined the sequence of insulin. It is still necessary to fragment the molecule by some method, examine the peptides, fragment by another method, examine these peptides, and attempt to put the puzzle together on the basis of partial identities in the various pieces. In principle, this may be done in two ways: in practice, neither method is used to the exclusion of the other.

The background of the first method is shown in Fig. 16. The protein would be cleaved first by procedure A into peptides I to V. After the peptides had been separated, the amino acid composition and sequence of each would be determined. In the ideal case, all residues that appear in the amino acid analysis of the protein will be accounted for. If the N- and C-terminal residues of the protein and perhaps a few sequences near the termini have been identified, it should be possible

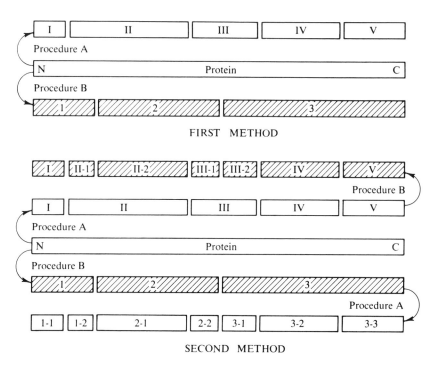

Figure 16. Principles of sequence determination by dissimilar partial cleavage and overlapping of sequences.

to place peptide I at the N terminus and peptide V at the C terminus, but the arrangement of peptides II to IV would not be established. Consequently, procedure B would be used to split the chain differently, and peptides 1 to 3 would be isolated, analyzed, and have their sequences determined. The order of peptides 1 to V should then be obvious.

The second method as shown in Fig. 16 would also cleave the protein by procedures A and B, separate the peptides, and determine their amino acid composition. However, rather than determine the sequence of each peptide, peptides I to V would be subjected individually to procedure B, peptides 1 to 3 individually to procedure A, and all peptides would be separated and analyzed. If the amino acid compositions were sufficiently unique (as many times they are), it should be possible to order peptides I to V. Thus, application of procedure B to peptide I would not alter the peptide. Peptide 1 would yield 1-1 and 1-2 by procedure A; 1-1 is equivalent to I and 1-2 to II-1 which arises from the action of procedure B on peptide II. Consequently, I and II must be linked. By reasoning further in this manner, all the pieces from I to V or 1-1 to 3-3 can be placed in order. The result will be many pieces of polypeptide chain of which the arrangement is known but of which the internal sequences are still unknown.

As noted above, neither method is used to the exclusion of the other in practice. Nor is the game played by waiting until all pieces are there to be arranged. Some peptides are short, and their residues can easily be placed in sequence. Others are long and require much effort before all residues can be arranged. Likewise, not all peptides from a given procedure can always be isolated. For example, in a more complex case, a peptide from procedure A may be missing or impure, and yet a peptide from procedure B will clearly be related to it when all other possibilities have been excluded. Knowledge about a sequence usually accumulates from a combination of both methods and frequently must be augmented by data from a third method of cleavage. Information may at one stage of investigation definitely place I and II in sequence as well as IV and V, but provide no evidence as to whether the complete sequence should be I-II-III-IV-V or I-II-IV-V-III. Nevertheless, by obtaining more and more data, uncertainties can usually be resolved and all residues placed in sequence.

We shall now consider ways by which partial cleavage of the polypeptide chain may be made in order to obtain the pieces of the puzzle.

REFERENCE

EDMAN, P., AND G. BEGG (1967), A Protein Sequenator, *European J. Biochem.*, **1**, 80.

9

METHODS FOR PARTIAL HYDROLYSIS
OF THE POLYPEPTIDE CHAIN

Although the ideas are not inherent in the use of overlapping sequences as we have discussed them in the preceding chapter, it is desirable that the peptides from a cleavage should not be too small and that a cleavage should be specific rather than random. If the peptides are too short, it will be difficult to obtain the length of overlapping that is necessary to place peptides together with confidence. If the cleavage is random, some bonds may split in one molecule of protein and others in another molecule so that the yield of any one will be reduced.

Unfortunately, few methods of cleaving the polypeptide chain are as specific as desirable. Therefore, it is necessary to use the best as well as the less satisfactory. Nevertheless, an impressive array of useful and potentially useful enzymatic and chemical methods of cleavage is now available.[1] Before discussing these, we shall consider chemical modifications of disulfide and sulfhydryl groups that may be worthwhile in some stage of the investigation in order to prevent undesirable side reactions.

MODIFICATION OF DISULFIDE AND SULFHYDRYL GROUPS

It has already been pointed out (Chapter 4) that cystine with its disulfide bond and cysteine with its sulfhydryl group form a redox system. In fact, the sulfhydryl group makes cysteine perhaps the most reactive residue in a protein or peptide. Consequently, if a protein with one or more sulfhydryl groups is partially hydrolyzed, they may easily be oxidized to disulfide bonds by atmospheric oxygen. Not only

---

[1] Hill's detailed review (1965) on the subject of this chapter is a ready source of many references.

References for Chapter 9, pp. 115–117.

will the product be a grouping that is foreign to the original protein, but if three different cysteinyl residues were present, the six products would confuse the issue further. On the other hand, if disulfide bridges are present in the protein, the peptides in a partial hydrolyzate may under some conditions undergo interchange such as A—S—S—B→ A—S—S—A + B—S—S—B (Chapter 13). Accordingly, disulfide and sulfhydryl groups are usually purposely altered to prevent such reactions. Several methods may be used to accomplish this.

Oxidation

Insulin contains two types of polypeptide chains that are held together by disulfide bridges. Sanger simplified the whole problem of determining the sequence of insulin by oxidizing these disulfide bonds to sulfonic acid groups and then separating the two chains. Hirs (1956) made a thorough investigation of procedures for oxidation with performic acid. The latter is first formed at room temperature by the action of hydrogen peroxide on anhydrous formic acid and then mixed at −10°C with a solution of the protein in formic acid. After several hours of reaction at low temperature, the reaction mixture is diluted with ice water and frozen. Reagents and solvents are then removed by lyophilization (freeze-drying).

Oxidation with performic acid converts both cystine and cysteine to cysteic acid and methionine to methionine sulfone. With the exception of tryptophan, other amino acids are not altered. Tryptophan is oxidized and, although the chain is not cleaved, peptides with the altered tryptophyl residue usually are not isolated. Although this limitation of oxidation must be recognized, it may not be too serious a handicap. There are few tryptophyl residues in most proteins, and peptides that contain them can usually be isolated after partial hydrolysis of either the unmodified or differently modified protein. It is well to point out that the same type of hydrolysis may have to be applied to several modifications of the protein before the complete sequence is known. The loss of tryptophyl peptides during oxidation may be offset by desirable properties of the cysteic acid peptides.

Carboxymethylation or Carbamidomethylation

Other modifications involve the reaction of the sulfhydryl group with a reagent that forms a thioether. If disulfide groups are present, reduction is first necessary. Even in the absence of disulfide groups, a reduction is desirable to reverse any intermolecular or intramolecular formation of disulfide bonds that may have occurred during the isolation and handling of the protein. Under these conditions, tryptophan is not altered.

$$\cdots \overset{H}{N}-CHR-CO-\overset{H}{N}-CH-CO-\overset{H}{N}-CHR'-CO\cdots + HS-CH_2-CH_2-OH \xrightarrow{pH\ 8.6}$$

$$(or\ HS-CH_2-CH_2-NH_2)$$

with side chain:
$$\begin{array}{c} CH_2 \\ | \\ S \\ | \\ S \\ | \\ CH_2 \\ \underset{\cdots\,N-CH-CO-N\,\cdots}{\overset{H\ \ |\ \ \ \ \ \ \ \ H}{}} \end{array}$$

$$\cdots \overset{H}{N}-CHR-CO-\overset{H}{N}-CH-CO-\overset{H}{N}-CHR'-CO\cdots + I-CH_2-COOH \xrightarrow{pH\ 8.6}$$

$$(NH_2)$$

with side chain:
$$\begin{array}{c} CH_2 \\ | \\ SH \\ + \\ SH \\ | \\ CH_2 \\ \underset{\cdots\,N-CH-CO-N\,\cdots}{\overset{H\ \ |\ \ \ \ \ \ \ \ H}{}} \end{array}$$

$$\cdots \overset{H}{N}-CHR-CO-\overset{H}{N}-CH-CO-\overset{H}{N}-CHR'-CO\cdots + \cdots \overset{H}{N}-CH-CO-\overset{H}{N}\cdots$$

with side chains:
$$\begin{array}{c} CH_2 \\ | \\ S-CH_2-COOH \\ (NH_2) \end{array} \qquad \begin{array}{c} S-CH_2-COOH \\ (NH_2) \\ | \\ CH_2 \end{array}$$

Reaction Scheme 10.

Reduction is commonly made with mercaptoethanol or mercaptoethylamine at pH 8.6 and room temperature in $8M$ urea or $5M$ guanidinium chloride, which denatures the protein and renders all groups accessible for reaction. Dithiothreitol is a recently introduced and odorless reducing agent. Addition of iodoacetic acid or iodoacetamide converts the sulfhydryl groups of both the protein and the reducing agent. Reaction Scheme 10 summarizes the course of the modification.

The properties of the product will depend upon whether iodoacetic acid or iodoacetamide is the reagent. The former introduces a negatively charged group, which may or may not be desirable, whereas the latter does not alter the charge. In either instance, complete acid hydrolysis of a protein or peptide so modified will yield carboxymethylcysteine, which may easily be determined quantitatively with an automatic amino acid analyzer.

These alkylating agents will also react with methionyl, histidyl, or lysyl residues, but these reactions can be minimized or avoided by proper control of conditions. Crestfield *et al.* (1963) have examined the reaction in detail.

Cyanoethylation

Sulfhydryl groups may also be altered by treatment with acrylonitrile by a procedure that has been described by Weil and Seibles (1961); thus

$$
\cdots N\!-\!\underset{H}{}\!CHR\!-\!CO\!-\!\underset{H}{N}\!-\!\underset{\underset{\underset{SH}{|}}{\overset{|}{CH_2}}}{CH}\!-\!CO\!-\!\underset{H}{N}\!-\!CHR'\!-\!CO\cdots + CH_2\!=\!CH\!-\!C\!\equiv\!N \xrightarrow[\substack{Room \\ temp. \\ 4\ hr}]{pH\ 8}
$$

$$
\cdots N\!-\!\underset{H}{}\!CHR\!-\!CO\!-\!\underset{H}{N}\!-\!\underset{\underset{\underset{S-CH_2-CH_2-C\equiv N}{|}}{\overset{|}{CH_2}}}{CH}\!-\!CO\!-\!\underset{H}{N}\!-\!CHR'\!-\!CO\cdots
$$

No evident side reactions occur when this reagent is used under these conditions (see also p. 103). In one application of the reaction, the insolubility of the product introduced complications into further study. Complete hydrolysis yields carboxyethylcysteine.

Aminoethylation

A third type of modification yields a product of rather different structure. Although aminoethylation is excellent for the modification of sulfhydryl groups, Lindley (1956), as we shall see below (p. 102), devised this modification with a different purpose in mind. Furthermore, the modifying reagent β-bromoethylamine which Lindley used has now been superseded by ethylenimine. Ethylenimine (Raftery and Cole, 1966) reacts with sulfhydryl groups as follows

$$\cdots\text{N—CHR—CO—N—CH—CO—N—CHR}'\text{—CO}\cdots + \text{H}_2\text{C}\text{—CH}_2 \xrightarrow[\substack{8M\text{ urea}\\ \text{Room temp.}}]{\text{pH 8}}$$

(with H above each N; side chain: CH_2—SH; epoxide-like group H_2C—CH_2 bridged by N—H)

$$\cdots\text{N—CHR—CO—N—CH—CO—N—CHR}'\text{—CO}\cdots$$

(with H above each N; side chain: CH_2—$\text{S—CH}_2\text{—CH}_2\text{—NH}_2$)

Reactions with other amino acid residues do not occur at this pH in the half hour that is necessary to complete the reaction. Basic groups are introduced into the protein by this procedure, and, as we shall see below, a point of cleavage with trypsin is produced. The product of complete acid hydrolysis is β-aminoethylcysteine.

S-Sulfo Derivatives

The so-called S-sulfo derivatives constitute still another type of modification. The reaction was studied by Swan (1957) and by Bailey and Cole (1959) and has been applied by Pechere *et al.* (1958) to trypsinogen and α-chymotrypsinogen. The S-sulfo compound is formed by the reaction with sulfite; thus,

$$\cdots\text{N—CHR—CO—N—CH—CO—N—CHR}'\text{—CO}\cdots + \text{SO}_3{}^{\ominus\ominus} \rightleftharpoons$$

(with H above each N; side chain: CH_2—S—S—CH_2—CH with $\cdots$N—CH—CO$\cdots$ and H above N)

$$\cdots\text{N—CHR—CO—N—CH—CO—N—CHR}'\text{—CO}\cdots$$

(with H above each N; side chain: CH_2—$\text{S—SO}_3{}^{\ominus}$ and $+$ $\text{S}^{\ominus}$—CH_2—CH with $\cdots$N—CH—CO$\cdots$ and H above N)

By oxidation in the presence of cupric ion, iodosobenzoate, or tetrathionate, the other sulfur of the disulfide bridge may be converted into the S-sulfo form also. Accordingly, the reaction is carried out at pH 7 or 10 and at room temperature or 38°C in $8M$ urea, which contains sodium sulfite and the oxidizing agent. This derivative is less stable than the alkylated compounds that we have considered above but has been successfully used. Prior to amino acid analysis, the S-sulfo peptides are oxidized to cysteic acid derivatives.

PARTIAL HYDROLYSIS BY ENZYMES

The only enzymes that need concern us here are the proteolytic enzymes—those that hydrolyze peptide bonds. Neither need we consider the mechanism of enzyme action. This topic is adequately discussed in textbooks of biochemistry and in compendia such as that of Dixon and Webb (1964).

The use of proteolytic enzymes in the determination of sequence is a purely practical one, because the object is to hydrolyze certain peptide bonds as completely and as specifically as possible. Consequently, in the first application of an enzyme to a determination of sequence, the extensive knowledge about enzymes is applied in a rather primitive way. Because the substrate is a complex one, the various hydrolyzable bonds are cleaved at different rates. As a result, there is a range rather than a well-defined optimum pH for the hydrolysis. One must, therefore, use rather arbitrary conditions that are based on data from simple substrates. Only when considerable knowledge of the structure of the protein has been obtained, may it be possible to apply profitably some of the nuances of information about enzyme action.

Although enzymes are now the most popular way of degrading a protein, it was not always so. Enzymatic action is, of course, reversible, because an enzyme not only can hydrolyze a peptide bond but also can form it. Hence, early investigators of sequence feared that the primary products of hydrolysis might recombine under the action of the enzyme into sequences that were not present in the original polypeptide chain. Sanger in his investigation of insulin approached the problem first with unspecific acidic hydrolysis and applied enzymes only in the later stages. However, the fear that a transpeptidation of this type would occur has not been realized. The equilibrium is so far on the side of hydrolysis that transpeptidation has never been observed either directly or by ambiguity in the results from enzymatic as compared to other types of cleavage. Consequently, enzymes have come to enjoy a privileged position in investigations of sequence. We shall now consider the properties of the more useful enzymes.

Prior Preparation—Denaturation

Because most proteolytic enzymes show only minimal action toward native proteins, all bonds that the enzyme is capable of cleaving are not cleaved. To achieve the desired end, the protein must be denatured before enzymatic digestion, that is, its native three-dimensional configuration must be disrupted. Whatever form the denaturation may take, its effect is generally assumed to be such that the molecule is unfolded (perhaps so completely as to form an extended polypeptide chain) and that all susceptible bonds are made accessible. Denaturation can be both reversible and irreversible. Some proteins, for example, are very sensitive even to mild influences, lose their native properties, and never regain them. Others may be treated with drastic denaturing conditions and yet be caused to regain their normal characteristics. Though alteration may have occurred under mild conditions, the denaturation may have been so slight that digestion may not be very complete. Consequently, denaturation before subjecting the protein to enzymatic action for sequence determination is usually made under vigorous conditions.

Many proteins are effectively denatured by heat. Often a dissolved protein will precipitate when a solution is heated to 100°C or less for some minutes, but other proteins may denature in a less obvious manner under these conditions. Enzymatic action can then be applied to such denatured proteins. That the protein may be insoluble does not usually interfere with the enzymatic digestion. As a rule the reaction occurs readily, and the insoluble protein dissolves partially or completely.

Strong solutions of urea ($8M$) or of guanidinium chloride ($6M$) are common means of denaturing. Most proteins are effectively denatured when dissolved in either solution. They usually remain in solution until the urea or guanidinium chloride is removed by dialysis or by molecular sieving with a column of Bio-Gel or Sephadex (see Chapter 3). Usually, the denaturing agent is removed before the enzymatic digestion because it can inactivate the enzyme also. In some instances, enzymatic digestion has been made in $2M$ urea at which concentration trypsin, for example, is still active.

Contaminants in urea can introduce undesirable side reactions. Especially under basic conditions, the reverse of the reaction by which Wöhler first produced urea occurs, and a slight amount of ammonium cyanate is formed. Reaction with amino groups will occur as in the cyanate method for N-terminal residues (Chapter 6). These carbamyl compounds can then interfere with other reactions later in the investigation. Deionization of the urea solution with a mixed-bed ion-exchange resin[2] will remove the cyanate.

Extremes of pH frequently denature proteins. Precipitation with strong trichloroacetic acid solutions is a well known effect. Such solvents as trifluoroacetic acid or anhydrous formic acid have also been used effectively.

If denaturation has resulted from prior operations, conditions of denaturation need not be applied specifically to a protein before enzymatic digestion. As we have already discussed, modification of sulfhydryl groups usually is preceded by reduction in strong urea solution. Consequently, the protein is not only modified but also denatured and is ready for enzymatic cleavage.

Trypsin

Trypsin is the most specific proteolytic enzyme in common use. Its application to problems of protein chemistry has been extremely widespread and accompanied by much success.

The enzyme occurs in the pancreas as the inactive precursor trypsinogen, which is activated by trypsin. During the process of activation, the hexapeptide Val-Asp-Asp-Asp-Asp-Lys is released from the N terminus of the single chain of trypsinogen which is made up of 229 residues (Chapter 14, p. 183).

Although many variations are possible, most hydrolyses with trypsin are made under rather similar conditions. Frequently, a 1 percent solution or suspension of the protein is hydrolyzed with trypsin equal to 0.5 to 1 percent of the protein by weight (a concentration of 0.005 to 0.01 percent). The pH is controlled (conveniently by pH-stat) at some value between 7.5 and 9.0 in most instances. The reaction usually is carried out over a period between an hour or two and a day either at room temperature or at 37°C.

The specificity of trypsin limits its action almost exclusively to peptide bonds associated with the carboxyl groups of lysine and arginine. Tryptic peptides, therefore, are expected to be C-terminal in lysine or arginine. In long hydrolyses, partial cleavage of some bonds associated with the carboxyl group of tryptophan has been observed.

---

[2] A mixed-bed resin has both anion- and cation-exchange resins and, therefore, can remove both cations and anions from a solution.

Although this type of cleavage has usually been attributed to contaminating chymotrypsin in the trypsin, this seems an unlikely explanation because cleavage at other bonds of equal susceptibility to chymotrypsin does not occur. Despite the fact that trypsin rarely hydrolyzes bonds other than those of lysine and arginine, it by no means splits all potential points of cleavage with equal speed or success. Thus, the rate of cleaving a -Lys-Pro- or an -Arg-Pro- bond is zero. If the sequence is -Asp-Lys- or -Asp-Arg-, the rate of hydrolysis is greatly reduced. Other combinations of residues with lysine or arginine seem to be almost completely cleaved in several hours under the conditions given above. Trypsin appears to be slowed or stopped in its action if the potential point of cleavage is near the N or C terminus of a chain. For example, four points of hydrolysis would be expected in a sequence such as -X-Arg-Arg-Lys-Lys-Y-. However, if the first hydrolysis gave -X-Arg-Arg and Lys-Lys-Y-, further anticipated hydrolyses may occur slowly or not at all. Perhaps the active site of the enzyme requires several residues on either side of the susceptible bond for effective binding and action.

Mention should be made of an enzyme that cleaves arginyl and lysyl bonds at such different rates that it appears to be virtually specific for the former. This enzyme termed clostripain by Labouesse (1960) was isolated from a *Clostridium* species. In experiments with the B chain of insulin, the Lys-Ala bond was cleaved at $\frac{1}{500}$ the rate of the Arg-Gly bond. In glucagon, the three types of bonds Arg-Arg, Arg-Ala, and Lys-Tyr were split at rates in the ratio 1 to $\frac{1}{7}$ to $\frac{1}{500}$. The enzyme is difficult to isolate, and its commercial unavailability has prevented other application.

Modification of Tryptic Action

With unimportant exceptions, trypsin is specific for those peptide bonds associated with the carboxyl groups of lysine and arginine. It is conceivably of advantage in fragmenting the polypeptide chain to be able to block the action of trypsin at one or the other common site of action, to cleave into peptides, to separate the peptides, to remove the blocking groups, to treat again with trypsin, to separate the peptides, and thus to determine which tryptic peptides are associated in some portion of the molecule. Another variant of this idea is to modify other residues to produce additional points of cleavage. A number of modifications have been proposed and applied with some or all of the above aims in mind. These will now be discussed.

AMINOETHYLATION

Reaction of sulfhydryl groups with ethylenimine to produce a β-aminoethylcysteinyl residue has been described on p. 96. Although the reaction protects from undesirable side reactions of cysteine, Lindley (1956) originally converted cysteine to this derivative in order to produce an extra point of cleavage for trypsin. The side chain, which is $-CH_2-S-CH_2-CH_2-NH_2$, differs from that of lysine, $-CH_2-CH_2-CH_2-CH_2-NH_2$, only in the substitution of $-S-$ for $-CH_2-$. Trypsin does not distinguish between the two, although the rate of cleaving aminoethylcysteinyl bonds is somewhat less than that of lysyl bonds. Thus, useful extra cleavage does indeed occur. The thioether bond of aminoethylcysteine is less susceptible to oxidation to the sulfoxide or sulfone than is that of methionine.

DITHIOCARBAMYLATION

Although carbon disulfide will react with amino groups, the lability of the compound prevented Leonis and Levy (1954) from devising a satisfactory method of sequential degradation. It was, however, the lability of the product that recommended it to Merigan *et al.* (1962) as a blocking group for the ε-amino group of lysine; the derivative

$$\cdots X-Y-Arg-A-B-\underset{\underset{NH_2}{|}}{Lys}-C-D-\underset{\underset{NH_2}{|}}{Lys}-E-F-Arg-G-H-Arg \cdots + CS_2 \xrightarrow[9-10]{pH}$$

$$\cdots X-Y-Arg-A-B-\underset{\underset{\underset{S}{\parallel}}{HN-C-SH}}{Lys}-C-D-\underset{\underset{\underset{S}{\parallel}}{HN-C-SH}}{Lys}-E-F-Arg-G-H-Arg \cdots \xrightarrow{Trypsin}$$

$$\cdots X-Y-Arg + A-B-\underset{\underset{\underset{S}{\parallel}}{HN-C-SH}}{Lys}-C-D-\underset{\underset{\underset{S}{\parallel}}{HN-C-SH}}{Lys}-E-F-Arg + G-H-Arg \xrightarrow[Aerate]{pH 2}$$

$$\cdots X-Y-Arg + A-B-\underset{\underset{NH_2}{|}}{Lys}-C-D-\underset{\underset{NH_2}{|}}{Lys}-E-F-Arg + G-H-Arg$$

Trypsin after isolation and determination of composition

$$A-B-\underset{\underset{NH_2}{|}}{Lys} + C-D-\underset{\underset{NH_2}{|}}{Lys} + E-F-Arg$$

Reaction Scheme 11.

is stable at alkaline pH where tryptic action would be employed, but the reaction is easily reversed at acid pH.

The course of the procedure is given in Reaction Scheme 11 where X, Y, etc. refer to various amino acid residues.

TRIFLUOROACETYLATION

Another procedure for temporarily blocking the ε-amino group of lysine has been proposed by Goldberger and Anfinsen (1962) who used ethyl thioltrifluoroacetate according to the reaction

$$\text{Protein}-\varepsilon NH_2 + F_3C-\overset{\overset{\displaystyle O}{\|}}{C}-S-CH_2-CH_3 \xrightarrow[25°C]{\text{pH 10}}$$

$$\text{Protein}-\varepsilon \overset{\displaystyle H}{N}-CO-CF_3 + C_2H_5SH$$

After tryptic hydrolysis and other operations, the trifluoroacetyl group may be removed at $0°C$ with $1M$ piperidine.

AMIDINATION

Hunter and Ludwig (1962) have used a reaction with methyl acetimidate to introduce a removable blocking group

$$\text{Protein}-\varepsilon NH_2 + CH_3-\overset{\overset{\displaystyle NH \cdot HCl}{\|}}{C}-O-CH_3 \rightarrow \text{Protein}-\varepsilon \overset{\displaystyle H}{\underset{\displaystyle |}{N}}-\overset{\overset{\displaystyle NH_2 \oplus}{\|}}{C}-CH_3 + CH_3OH$$

The reaction was carried out at pH 9 and room temperature with the successive additions of several portions of the easily hydrolyzed methyl acetimidate hydrochloride over a period of several hours. At the appropriate point, removal may be made with an ammonia-acetic acid buffer at pH 11.3 over a period of 8 hr (Ludwig and Byrne, 1962).

CYANOETHYLATION

Although the reaction was applied in another context, the data of Riehm and Scheraga (1966) show that an irreversible blocking of ε-amino groups occurs if acrylonitrile is used. One or two molecules may react; thus,

$$\text{Protein}-\varepsilon NH_2 + CH_2{=}CH-C{\equiv}N \rightarrow$$

$$\text{Protein}-\varepsilon \overset{\displaystyle H}{N}-CH_2-CH_2-C{\equiv}N + \text{Protein}-\varepsilon N \overset{\displaystyle CH_2-CH_2-C{\equiv}N}{\underset{\displaystyle CH_2-CH_2-C{\equiv}N}{\diagup}}$$

The conditions were $0.4M$ acrylonitrile at $2°C$ and pH 9.2 for seven days. It will be recalled that sulfhydryl groups also react with acrylonitrile (p. 96) so that they of necessity would also be modified. However, the reaction of ε-amino groups proceeds much more slowly, and it is possible to react sulfhydryl groups selectively.

The permanence of this group as well as the reaction of one or two molecules per amino group would seem to limit the utility of the reagent.

REACTION WITH BENZIL OR CYCLOHEXADIONE

All of the above reagents modify the ε-amino group of lysine. Two reagents, both 1,2-diones, have been proposed by Itano and co-workers for altering the guanidino group of arginine (Itano and Gottlieb, 1963; Toi et al., 1965). The blocking group is not removable from either product. Because of the aqueous insolubility of benzil, the reaction is

Reaction Scheme 12.

carried out in 70–80 percent alcohol that is $0.2M$ in potassium hydroxide. With cyclohexadione, in aqueous $0.2M$ potassium hydroxide overnight at room temperature, the reaction depicted in Reaction Scheme 12 takes place. Although arginine can not be regenerated, the product is stable to hydrolysis and is, therefore, quantitatively determinable in a modified protein or peptide.

King (1966) has modified arginine with malonyl aldehyde. The reaction in $10N$ hydrochloric acid produces

$$
\begin{array}{l}
\text{HC} \overset{\displaystyle\overset{\text{H}}{\text{C}}}{=}\text{N} \qquad\qquad\qquad\qquad \text{NH}_2 \\
\qquad\qquad\qquad\qquad\qquad\;\; | \\
\text{HC}\underset{\text{N}}{\searrow}{}_{\text{N}}\diagup \text{C}\overset{\text{H}}{-}\text{N}-(\text{CH}_2)_3-\text{CH}-\text{COOH}
\end{array}
$$

Although these modifications have been proposed, little application has yet been made of them to problems of sequence determination. Consequently, their usefulness has yet to be established.

Chymotrypsin

Chymotrypsin like trypsin occurs as an inactive zymogen in the pancreatic secretion. There are considerable similarities in the structures of the two zymogens. Activation of chymotrypsinogen first by trypsin and then by chymotrypsin yields α-chymotrypsin with the release of the dipeptides Ser-Arg and Thr-Asn from the original 245 residues. α-Chymotrypsin (see Chapter 14, p. 172) has three chains of diverse length that are held together by disulfide bridges.

Chymotrypsin is used to cleave the polypeptide chains of denatured proteins under conditions that are essentially identical to those that have been described for trypsin (p. 100). However, the type of bond that is hydrolyzed is different, and the specificity is less. Chymotrypsin splits most rapidly those bonds associated with the carboxyl groups of tryptophan, tyrosine, phenylalanine, and leucine. In addition, cleavage occurs at bonds associated with methionine, asparagine, glutamine, histidine, and, to a lesser extent, threonine and lysine. If we examine the action of chymotrypsin on a variety of proteins, it may be concluded that most bonds associated with the aromatic amino acids and leucine will be hydrolyzed, but that bonds adjacent to the other amino acids enumerated above will be incompletely and variably hydrolyzed under normal conditions. As in the case of trypsin, the bond between X and proline in the sequence -X-Pro- will not be hydrolyzed by chymotrypsin, and a bond near aspartic acid certainly will be cleaved more slowly. If several potentially susceptible bonds are near each other, one will usually be preferentially hydrolyzed; the others because of proximity to a terminus then often remain unhydrolyzed. As an example of this type, consider a sequence of the β chain of human adult hemoglobin, which is

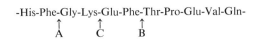

-His-Phe-Gly-Lys-Glu-Phe-Thr-Pro-Glu-Val-Gln-

In the intact chain, chymotrypsin acts upon bonds A and B. However, if bond C is cleaved by trypsin and chymotrypsin is then allowed to act on the tryptic peptide with the sequence Glu-Phe-etc., bond B does not hydrolyze. One can suggest that in the case of the tryptic peptide both the proximity to the N terminus as well as the negatively charged amino acid may be influential in preventing the action. On the other hand, in the intact chain the negative charge of the glutamyl residue may be neutralized by the lysyl residue. The environment obviously has an important influence in determining whether or not a bond will cleave.

Pepsin

Although trypsin and chymotrypsin are the most useful enzymes for the study of sequence, pepsin has also been of value. When the inactive pepsinogen is activated by adjusting a solution to pH 2, 42 of approximately 360 residues are removed. The resulting pepsin contains only one lysyl and two arginyl residues (Rajagopalan *et al.*, 1966). Pepsin is active at acidic rather than at basic pH as are trypsin and chymotrypsin. This fact alone has increased the value of pepsin in sequence studies, as we shall see when the problem of determining the position of disulfide bridges is considered in Chapter 13. Prior denaturation of the protein is usually unnecessary because the pH of the medium (1.5–2.0) itself effectively denatures most proteins.

The action of pepsin parallels that of chymotrypsin to a degree with the important distinction that cleavage of bonds associated with the amino rather than the carboxyl group of tyrosine or phenylalanine is to be expected. Nevertheless, pepsin exhibits far more random cleavage, and examples of the hydrolysis of almost any type of bond can be adduced.

Other Enzymes

Other proteolytic enzymes such as papain or subtilopeptidase (subtilisin) may be employed. The latter is a bacterial proteinase from

Bacillus subtilis. Bacterial proteinases are available commercially under trade names such as "Pronase" or "Nagarse." These enzymes have seen little application to intact proteins for cleavage into peptides, because their action tends to be so drastic that rather small peptides are produced. Not only is the mixture complex and the peptides difficult to purify, but their short length does not give sufficient overlapping in establishing sequence.

They can, however, be useful in hydrolyzing peptides from other sources into smaller fragments. For example, a fairly long tryptic peptide may have no potential points of cleavage by chymotrypsin, and therefore the determination of its complete sequence may be difficult. The more random action of papain or a bacterial proteinase may have a welcome result.

Further comments about the use of enzymes will be made in later discussions (Chapter 11, p. 144 ff).

CHEMICAL CLEAVAGE

As methods of amino acid analysis became available and as procedures for determining sequence were being devised, enzymatic methods of hydrolysis played a lesser role than partial hydrolysis in strong acid. This reluctance to use enzymes was in part due to the fear of transpeptidation that has been mentioned above (p. 98). Although complete hydrolysis of peptide bonds occurs in $6N$ hydrochloric acid at 110°C in 24 hr or less, at room temperature or slightly above this concentration of acid will only partially hydrolyze the protein in the course of several days. The peptides in the mixture can then be separated and used for the determination of sequence. The method is successful because the various bonds hydrolyze at different rates; some like those associated with the amino groups of serine and threonine are almost invariably cleaved, whereas others associated with valine or isoleucine are very resistant to hydrolysis. Because the method lacks specificity, the yield of any peptide is reduced. Furthermore, free amino acids are produced in considerable amount to lower the yield even more. Consequently, partial acidic hydrolysis has given way, in general, to enzymatic hydrolysis with its greater specificity and higher yields.

However, much effort has been expended in attempts to use the chemical properties in various side chains of the amino acids to induce a cleavage of the polypeptide chain either N- or C-terminal to the corresponding residue. Witkop (1961) in discussing the subject in detail has differentiated between preferential (that is, competitive, hydrolytic) cleavage and selective (that is, noncompetitive, nonhydro-lytic) cleavage. Methods of chemical splitting are designed to be selective.

If a selective method can be applied to residues which are small in number in the protein, large pieces (on the average) with extensive overlaps may be obtained. In a sense, one may have broken a large protein into several smaller ones.

If one examines the side chains of the amino acids, it is apparent that the aliphatic groups in glycine, alanine, valine, isoleucine, leucine, and proline as well as phenylalanine offer few points of attack. The other residues have potentially reactive points and may be grouped in categories of some similarity as aspartic and glutamic acids (as well as asparagine and glutamine); lysine and arginine; tyrosine, tryptophan, and histidine; cystine, cysteine, and methionine; and serine and threonine. Actually, it has been possible to take advantage of the reactivity of only a few of these, and the procedures are not all equally successful. We shall now consider the various reactions.

Reaction with Cyanogen Bromide

The cleavage of the polypeptide chain with cyanogen bromide is the most useful chemical method yet devised. The reaction is believed to take the course in Reaction Scheme 13 (Gross and Witkop, 1962). Prior to the reaction, the protein is dissolved in a solvent such as $0.1N$ hydrochloric acid, 70 percent trifluoroacetic acid, or 70 percent formic acid. The cyanogen bromide is added in large excess (30 equivalents) and allowed to react at room temperature for 16 to 24 hr. The reaction product is easily isolated by diluting with water and lyophilizing to remove the solvent, methyl thiocyanate, and excess cyanogen bromide.

The method has had wider and more successful application than any other method of chemical cleavage. The reaction is almost quantitative, excess reagent has no deleterious effect, side reactions seem to be almost nonexistent, and the simple requirements for isolation are attractive. Because the methionine content of most proteins is relatively small, the number of peptides will be small.

Refluxing with Dilute Acetic or Hydrochloric Acids

Quite a few years ago, Partridge and Davis (1950) observed that refluxing a protein with dilute acetic acid resulted in the almost selective release of free aspartic acid to the exclusion of other free amino acids. Methods were not available at the time to take full advantage of this

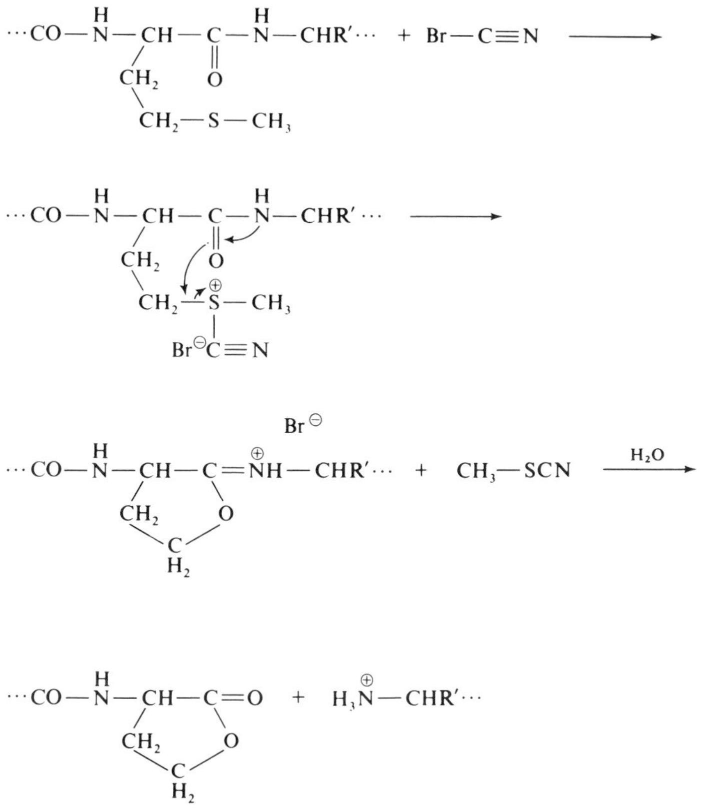

$$\cdots CO-\overset{\text{H}}{\underset{}{N}}-CH-\overset{\text{H}}{\underset{}{C}}-\overset{\text{H}}{\underset{}{N}}-CHR'\cdots \ +\ Br-C\equiv N \longrightarrow$$

with the CH residue bearing:
$$\begin{array}{c} CH_2 \\ \backslash \\ CH_2-S-CH_3 \end{array}$$
and the C bearing $\parallel O$

$$\cdots CO-\overset{\text{H}}{\underset{}{N}}-CH-\overset{}{C}-\overset{\text{H}}{\underset{}{N}}-CHR'\cdots \longrightarrow$$

$$\begin{array}{c} CH_2 \\ \backslash \\ CH_2\overset{\oplus}{-}S-CH_3 \\ \mid \\ Br^{\ominus}C\equiv N \end{array}$$

$$Br^{\ominus}$$

$$\cdots CO-\overset{\text{H}}{\underset{}{N}}-CH-\overset{\oplus}{C}=NH-CHR'\cdots \ +\ CH_3-SCN \xrightarrow{\ H_2O\ }$$

$$\begin{array}{c} CH_2 \quad\quad O \\ \backslash \quad\quad / \\ C \\ H_2 \end{array}$$

$$\cdots CO-\overset{\text{H}}{\underset{}{N}}-CH-C=O \ +\ H_3\overset{\oplus}{N}-CHR'\cdots$$

$$\begin{array}{c} CH_2 \quad\quad O \\ \backslash \quad\quad / \\ C \\ H_2 \end{array}$$

Homoserine lactone

Reaction Scheme 13.

fact. In recent years, it has again received attention and investigation. The reaction for which various mechanisms have been proposed follows this over-all course:

$$\cdots \text{X-Y-Asp-A-B}\cdots \rightarrow \cdots \text{X-Y} + \text{Asp} + \text{A-B}\cdots$$

where X, Y, A, and B are amino acid residues of any kind.

Originally a 0.25M solution of acetic acid or oxalic acid at 100°C was used (Partridge and Davis, 1950), but it was soon learned that low pH rather than the presence of an organic acid is the essential feature. Schultz and collaborators (1962) have employed 0.03N hydrochloric acid at 100°C for various periods of time. Under these conditions, not only aspartic acid but also asparagine (after initial hydrolysis to aspartic acid) is released.

In the author's laboratory, the originally suggested 0.25M acetic acid under reflux has proved most successful. Such a solution is more specific than 0.03N hydrochloric acid for aspartic acid, because asparagine is cleaved much more slowly and other amino acids almost not at all. Figure 17 shows the release of aspartic acid from catalase protein by refluxing 0.25M acetic acid in a solution that contained one

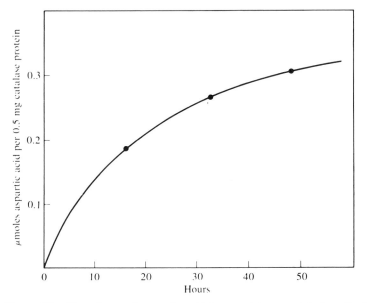

Figure 17. The release of aspartic acid from catalase protein by refluxing 0.25 M acetic acid.

mg of protein per ml. At appropriate times, a sample was removed and examined for free amino acids by means of the automatic analyzer. Amino acids other than aspartic acid were inconsequential in amount. An examination of the peptides showed the expected cleavages; in 48 hr, some asparaginyl bonds had cleaved.

Acyl Shift

If, because of the presence of a certain type of residue, the peptide bond can be converted into a different type of bond, specific cleavage might be possible because the chemical properties of this bond would differ from those of the usual peptide bond. It has long been known (Elliott, 1952) that in a strong acid under anhydrous conditions the carbonyl group will shift from its bond with the amino group of serine to form an ester linkage with the hydroxyl group of serine; thus,

$$\cdots CHR-CO-\underset{\underset{HOCH_2}{|}}{\overset{H}{N}}-CH-CO-NH\cdots \xrightarrow[\text{Anhydrous}]{(H^{\oplus})} \xleftarrow{(OH^{\ominus})}$$

$$\overset{\oplus}{H_3N}-CH-CO-NH\cdots$$
$$\cdots CHR-CO-O-\underset{|}{CH_2}$$

Under mild basic conditions the cleavage of the ester bond but not of peptide bonds could be accomplished,

$$\overset{\oplus}{H_3N}-CH-CO-NH\cdots \xrightarrow{(OH^{\ominus})} \cdots CHR-COOH$$
$$\cdots CHR-CO-O-\underset{|}{CH_2}$$

$$+ \quad \underset{HO-\underset{|}{CH_2}}{H_2N-CH-CO-NH\cdots}$$

but it is also under the same conditions that the reaction is reversed. Consequently, the amino group should be blocked before the cleavage is attempted.

Lenard and Hess (1964) in a study of this reaction used anhydrous hydrofluoric acid as the medium in which to produce the shift, whereas sulfuric acid has been a common solvent in other investigations. Prior to cleavage, the newly exposed amino groups were blocked by formylation, and the cleavage was accomplished in $1M$ piperidine at 0°C for 2 hr. The formyl blocking group would, of course, preclude any sequential degradation of the newly formed peptides by means of the Edman procedure. Smyth and Stark (1966) have suggested that cyanate can be used to block with the carbamyl group and thus leave the way open to further degradation.

Despite the effort that has been expended in attempts to devise a practical procedure, the main problem still appears to be in obtaining a satisfactory and complete acyl shift.

Cyanide and Cystinyl Residues

Under proper conditions cyanide, as shown by Catsimpoolas and Wood (1966), will cleave the disulfide bond and one peptide bond that was associated with an amino group of the original cystinyl residue (Reaction Scheme 14).

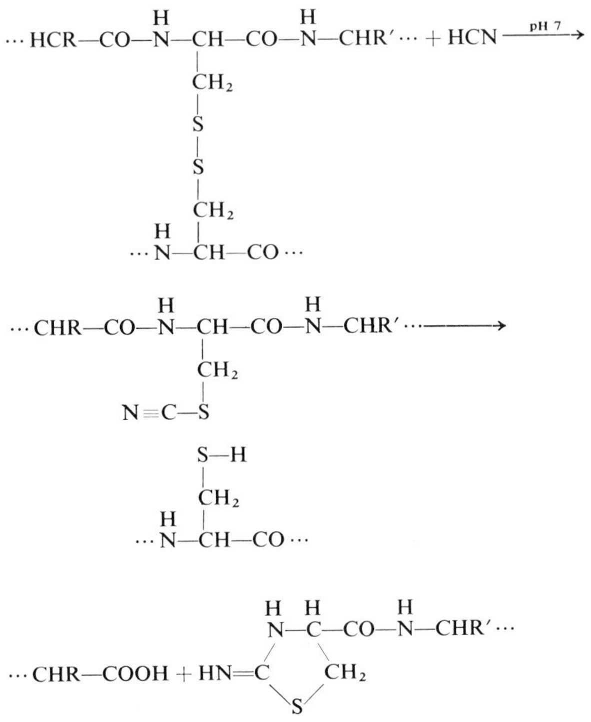

$$\cdots HCR-CO-\overset{H}{N}-CH-CO-\overset{H}{N}-CHR' \cdots + HCN \xrightarrow{\;pH\,7\;}$$

$$\begin{array}{c} | \\ CH_2 \\ | \\ S \\ | \\ S \\ | \\ CH_2 \\ H\ | \\ \cdots N-CH-CO\cdots \end{array}$$

$$\cdots CHR-CO-\overset{H}{N}-CH-CO-\overset{H}{N}-CHR' \cdots \longrightarrow$$

$$\begin{array}{c} | \\ CH_2 \\ | \\ N{=}C-S \\ \\ S-H \\ | \\ CH_2 \\ H\ | \\ \cdots N-CH-CO\cdots \end{array}$$

$$\cdots CHR-COOH + HN{=}C \overset{\overset{\displaystyle H\ H \qquad\quad H}{N-C-CO-N-CHR' \cdots}}{\underset{\displaystyle S}{\diagup \quad CH_2 \diagdown}}$$

2-Iminothiazolidine-4-carboxylic acid

Reaction Scheme 14.

The scission is asymmetrical. The portion with the sulfhydryl group must be oxidized and again reacted with cyanide if the reaction is to go to completion. For successful application to proteins, careful modification of conditions would be required as the authors point out.

Reductive Cleavage at Prolyl Residues

The imide bond associated with proline is distinctly different from the other peptide bonds in its chemical properties. Although the normal peptide bond is unaltered under reductive conditions, reductive cleavage of the polypeptide can occur according to the following reaction when the imino group of an imino acid is involved in the peptide bond:

$$\cdots CHR-CO-N-\overset{\overbrace{}}{CH}-CO-\overset{H}{N}-CHR'\cdots \quad \xrightarrow{\ (H)\ }$$

$$\left[\begin{array}{c} \cdots CHR-CH_2OH \\ + \\ \cdots CHR-CHO \end{array}\right] \quad + \quad HN-\overset{\overbrace{}}{CH}-CO-\overset{H}{N}-CHR'\cdots$$

Several methods of reduction include lithium in methylamine (Patchornik *et al.*, 1964), lithium aluminum hydride (Ruttenberg *et al.*, 1964), and sodium in liquid ammonia (Wilchek *et al.*, 1965).

Although the reaction appears to proceed satisfactorily under some conditions, little practical use has been made of it.

Cleavage through Dehydroalanyl Residues

A method of cleavage that requires an initial alteration of cysteinyl residues has been proposed and applied by Patchornik and collaborators (Patchornik and Sokolovsky, 1964; Sokolovsky *et al.*, 1964). The sulfhydryl group is first selectively dinitrophenylated at pH 6. Under basic conditions, dinitrothiophenol is removed, and the cysteinyl residue is converted to a dehydroalanyl residue. Cleavage is then made at pH 2. Reaction Scheme 15 shows the series of conversions.

$$\cdots CHR-CO-\overset{H}{N}-\underset{\underset{\underset{SH}{|}}{\underset{CH_2}{|}}}{CH}-CO-\overset{H}{N}-CHR'\cdots \quad + \quad DNFB \quad \xrightarrow{pH\ 6}$$

$$\cdots CHR-CO-\overset{H}{N}-\underset{\underset{\underset{S-DNP}{|}}{\underset{CH_2}{|}}}{CH}-CO-\overset{H}{N}-CHR'\cdots \quad \xrightarrow{OH^{\ominus}}$$

$$\underset{NO_2}{\overset{S^{\ominus}}{\underset{}{\bigcirc}}}NO_2 \quad + \quad \cdots CHR-CO-\overset{H}{N}-\underset{\underset{CH_2}{\|}}{C}-CO-\overset{H}{N}-CHR'\cdots \quad \xrightarrow[\substack{100° \\ 2hr}]{pH\ 2}$$

$$\cdots CHR-CO-\overset{H}{N}H \quad + \quad CH_3-CO-CO-\overset{H}{N}-CHR'\cdots$$

Reaction Scheme 15.

When this reaction was applied to ribonuclease (Patchornik and Sokolovsky, 1964a), the protein had to be acetylated before the reactions could be successfully carried out. As a result, the products of the cleavage were derivatives. As such, they would be obstacles in the way of applying other procedures if the method were used with a protein of unknown sequence.

Potentially, a similar series of reactions could be used if a seryl residue were first tosylated

Oxidation with N-Bromosuccinimide

Oxidation with N-bromosuccinimide potentially will cleave the polypeptide chain wherever the grouping

occurs: phenylalanine, tyrosine, tryptophan, and histidine all contain it. The reactions are believed to follow the course in Reaction Scheme 16.

Shaltiel and Patchornik (1963) have discussed the reaction in some detail, and references may be found there to other uses of the method. Actually, phenylalanine does not react whereas tyrosine and tryptophan react rapidly. The course of the conversion has been followed spectro-photometrically to "titrate" and thus to determine the number of tryptophyl residues in a protein. It is reported that by proper variation in conditions the reaction may be made specific for tryptophan, tyrosine, or histidine. Although potentially useful, the method has not yet been applied with success to problems of sequence determination.

Comments

Although a variety of methods of chemical cleavage have been proposed, they are for the most part untried except on model compounds and on peptides and proteins of known structure. The reaction

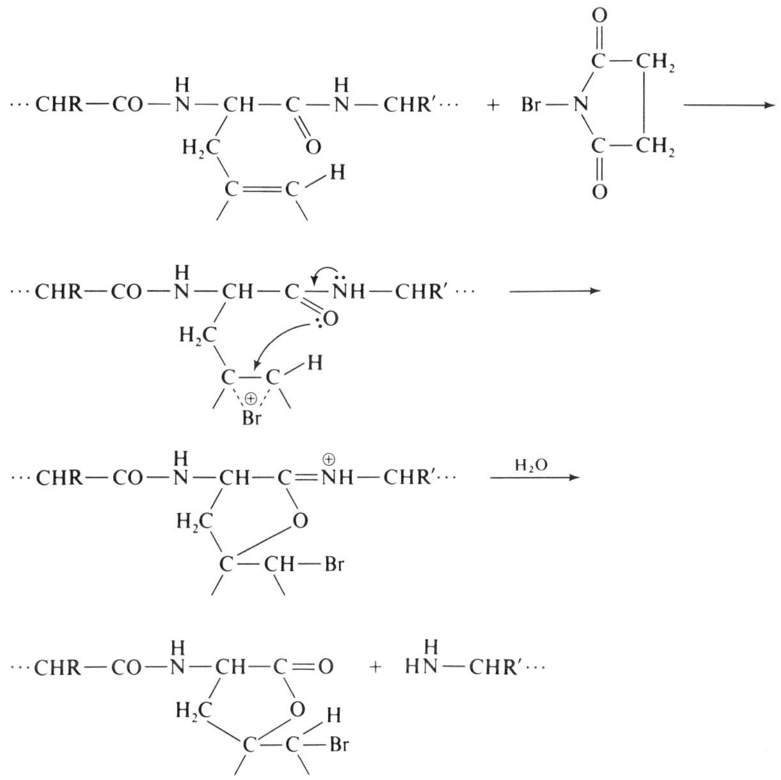

Reaction Scheme 16.

with cyanogen bromide and the hydrolysis with acetic acid have been applied with the greatest success. In most other instances, the authors themselves are free to admit the shortcomings of their method. Although not all have been successful, many clever procedures have been devised, and it is not too much to expect that other satisfactory methods will be forthcoming.

REFERENCES

BAILEY, J. L., AND R. D. COLE (1959), Studies on the Reaction of Sulfite with Proteins, *J. Biol. Chem.*, **234**, 1733.

CATSIMPOOLAS, N., AND J. L. WOOD (1966), Specific Cleavage of Cystine Peptides by Cyanide, *J. Biol. Chem.*, **241**, 1790.

CRESTFIELD, A. M., S. MOORE, AND W. H. STEIN (1963), The Preparation and

Enzymatic Hydrolysis of Reduced and *S*-Carboxymethylated Proteins, *J. Biol. Chem.*, **238**, 622.

DIXON, M., AND E. C. WEBB (1964), *Enzymes*, 2nd ed., New York, Academic Press.

ELLIOTT, D. F. (1952), A Search for Specific Chemical Methods for Fission of Peptide Bonds. I. The *N*-Acyl to *O*-Acyl Transformation in the Degradation of Silk Fibroin, *Biochem. J.*, **50**, 542.

GOLDBERGER, R. F., AND C. B. ANFINSEN (1962), The Reversible Masking of Amino Groups in Ribonuclease and Its Possible Usefulness in the Synthesis of the Protein, *Biochemistry*, **1**, 401.

GROSS, E., AND B. WITKOP (1962), Nonenzymatic Cleavage of Peptide Bonds: The Methionine Residues in Bovine Pancreatic Ribonuclease, *J. Biol. Chem.*, **237**, 1856.

HILL, R. L. (1965), Hydrolysis of Proteins, *Adv. Protein Chem.*, **20**, 37.

HIRS, C. H. W. (1956), The Oxidation of Ribonuclease with Performic Acid, *J. Biol. Chem.*, **219**, 611.

HUNTER, M. J., AND M. L. LUDWIG (1962), The Reaction of Imidoesters with Proteins and Related Small Molecules, *J. Am. Chem. Soc.*, **84**, 3491.

ITANO, H. A., AND A. J. GOTTLIEB (1963), Blocking of Tryptic Cleavage of Arginyl Bonds by the Chemical Modification of the Guanido Group with Benzil, *Biochem. Biophys. Res. Commun.*, **12**, 405.

KING, T. P. (1966), Selective Chemical Modification of Arginyl Residues, *Biochemistry*, **5**, 3454.

LABOUESSE, B. (1960), L'Hydrolyse de Glucagon per la Clostripaine, *Bull. Soc. Chim. Biol.*, **42**, 1293 and related papers.

LENARD, J., AND G. P. HESS (1964), An Approach to the Specific Cleavage of Peptide Bonds. II. Specific Cleavage of Peptide Chains Based on the Hydrogen Fluoride Induced Nitrogen to Oxygen Acyl Shift, *J. Biol. Chem.*, **239**, 3275.

LEONIS, J., AND A. L. LEVY (1954), A Method for the Controlled Degradation of Peptides Using Carbon Disulphide. Part I. Development of the Method, *Compt. Rend. Trav. Lab. Carlsberg, Ser. chim.*, **29**, 57.

LINDLEY, H. (1956), A New Synthetic Substrate for Trypsin and its Application to the Determination of the Amino-Acid Sequence of Proteins, *Nature*, **178**, 647.

LUDWIG, M. L., AND R. BYRNE (1962), Reversible Blocking of Protein Amino Groups by the Acetimidyl Group, *J. Am. Chem. Soc.*, **84**, 4160.

MERIGAN, T. C., W. J. DREYER, AND A. BERGER (1962), A Technique for the Specific Cleavage of Arginyl Bonds by Trypsin, *Biochim. Biophys. Acta*, **62**, 122.

PARTRIDGE, S. M., AND H. F. DAVIS (1950), Preferential Release of Aspartic Acid during the Hydrolysis of Proteins, *Nature*, **165**, 62.

PATCHORNIK, A., AND M. SOKOLOVSKY (1964), Nonenzymatic Cleavages of Peptide Chains at the Cysteine and Serine Residues through their Conversion into Dehydroalanine. I. Hydrolytic and Oxidative Cleavage of Dehydroalanine Residues, *J. Am. Chem. Soc.*, **86**, 1206.

PATCHORNIK, A., AND M. SOKOLOVSKY (1964a), Chemical Interactions between Lysine and Dehydroalanine in Modified Bovine Pancreatic Ribonuclease, *J. Am. Chem. Soc.*, **86**, 1860.

PATCHORNIK, A., M. WILCHEK, AND S. SARID (1964), Chemical Cleavage of Proline Peptide Bonds, *J. Am. Chem. Soc.*, **86**, 1457.

PECHERE, J.-F., G. H. DIXON, R. H. MAYBURY, AND H. NEURATH (1958), Cleavage of Disulfide Bonds in Trypsinogen and α-Chymotrypsinogen, *J. Biol. Chem.*, **233**, 1364.

RAFTERY, M. A., AND R. D. COLE (1966), On the Aminoethylation of Proteins, *J. Biol. Chem.*, **241**, 3457.

RAJAGOPALAN, T. G., S. MOORE, AND W. H. STEIN (1966), Pepsin from Pepsinogen —Preparation and Properties, *J. Biol. Chem.*, **241**, 4940.

RIEHM, J. P., AND H. A. SCHERAGA (1966), Structural Studies of Ribonuclease. XX. Acrylonitrile. A Reagent for Blocking the Amino Groups of Lysine Residues in Ribonuclease, *Biochemistry*, **5**, 93.

RUTTENBERG, M. A., T. P. KING, AND L. C. CRAIG (1964), Cleavage of Peptide Proline Bonds by Lithium Aluminum Hydride, *Biochemistry*, **3**, 758.

SCHULTZ, J., H. ALLISON, AND M. GRICE (1962), Specificity of the Cleavage of Proteins by Dilute Acid. I. Release of Aspartic Acid from Insulin, Ribonuclease, and Glucagon, *Biochemistry*, **1**, 694.

SHALTIEL, S., AND A. PATCHORNIK (1963), Cleavage of Histidyl Peptide Bonds by *N*-Bromosuccinimide, *J. Am. Chem. Soc.*, **85**, 2799.

SMYTH, D. G., AND G. R. STARK (1966), Quantitative Blocking of Amino Groups in Acid Solution by Carbamylation, *Anal. Biochem.*, **14**, 152.

SOKOLOVSKY, M., T. SADEH, AND A. PATCHORNIK (1964), Nonenzymatic Cleavage of Peptide Chains at the Cysteine and Serine Residues through their Conversion of Dehydroalanine (DHAL). II. The Specific Chemical Cleavage of Cysteinyl Peptides, *J. Am. Chem. Soc.*, **86**, 1212.

SWAN, J. M. (1957), Thiols, Disulphides, and Thiosulphates: Some New Reactions and Possibilities in Peptide and Protein Chemistry, *Nature*, **180**, 643.

TOI, K., E. BYNUM, E. NORRIS, AND H. A. ITANO (1965), Chemical Modification of Arginine with 1,2-Cyclohexandione, *J. Biol. Chem.*, **240**, PC3455.

WEIL, L., AND T. S. SEIBLES (1961), Reaction of Reduced Disulfide Bonds in α-Lactalbumin and β-Lactoglobulin with Acrylonitrile, *Arch. Biochem. Biophys.*, **95**, 470.

WILCHEK, M., S. SARID, AND A. PATCHORNIK (1965), Use of Sodium in Liquid Ammonia for Cleavage of N-Proline Peptides, *Biochim. Biophys. Acta*, **104**, 616.

WITKOP, B., (1961), Nonenzymatic Methods for the Preferential and Selective Cleavage and Modification of Proteins, *Adv. Protein Chem.*, **16**, 221.

10

THE SEPARATION OF PEPTIDES

The methods of cleavage that we have discussed in the preceding chapter are of little use in the determination of sequence unless the peptides so produced can be separated. Although some of these methods have been known for many years and have been used to produce peptides, the inability to isolate individual peptides in pure form blocked completely any progress in identifying sequences. Progress became possible and began only when chromatography was applied and increasingly used in all procedures for sequence determination.

Paper chromatographic methods had been successfully applied to the qualitative separation and identification of amino acids by Consden, Gordon, and Martin (1944) some years before Sanger applied them to the separation of peptides in his successful determination of the sequence of insulin. Although a major portion of Sanger's work was carried out on paper chromatograms, his initial and partial separations used not only column chromatography on an ion-exchange resin and on charcoal but also some electrophoresis.

Although paper chromatography is still a widely used procedure in all phases of sequence investigation, its most ardent devotees generally have turned to column chromatography as they have investigated more and more complex proteins.

Two severe limitations of paper methods are the relatively small amounts that can be chromatographed and the generally poor recovery of peptides from the paper. It must not be inferred that column chromatography is without problems: one of them is the poor recovery of certain types of peptides.

It is difficult to present a satisfactory discussion of methods for the separation of peptides. Standard procedures are not common because of the individuality of the proteins themselves and of the investigators

118 References for Chapter 10, pp. 134–145.

each of whom seems to have procedures that he finds to be eminently successful. As a point of departure for discussing the separation of peptides, let us consider the determination of the amino acid sequence of adult human hemoglobin.

THE EXAMPLE OF HEMOGLOBIN

Hemoglobin can easily be obtained in quantity, is readily purified, and, of course, is obviously visible. Any one or all of these characteristics no doubt endeared this protein to many investigators, and as a result probably more is known about hemoglobin than about any other protein. Nevertheless, investigation was accelerated when Pauling, Itano, Singer, and Wells (1949) discovered that, in the disease known as sickle cell anemia, the hemoglobin differed from that in the majority of human adults. From electrophoretic behavior, amino acid composition, and other information, it was concluded that the difference between the two hemoglobins was small. In his investigation of the dissimilarity between normal human hemoglobin (hemoglobin A) and sickle cell anemia hemoglobin (hemoglobin S), Ingram (1956) devised an extremely useful method that is known formally as "peptide mapping" and colloquially as "fingerprinting."

Peptide Mapping or Fingerprinting

Behind the idea of fingerprinting (at least as it was initially applied to hemoglobins A and S) lay three pieces of information:

(1) the specificity of tryptic action,
(2) the separation of peptides on paper by chromatography and/or electrophoresis, and
(3) the small difference (which involves a charge difference) between hemoglobins A and S.

It was reasoned that because the difference was small almost all corresponding tryptic peptides in individual hydrolyzates of the two proteins would behave identically but that corresponding peptides of different sequence would behave distinctively.

The principles of peptide fingerprinting are shown in Fig. 18. Two pieces of heavy filter paper sheet are cut, dipped in pyridine–acetic acid buffer at pH 6.4, and laid upon a glass sheet in such a way that the tabs hang over the edge into electrode vessels. The tryptic hydrolyzate of about 2 mg of hemoglobin A is placed at A and of hemoglobin S at S, and the whole is covered with a second glass sheet. The dotted lines outline the position of the glass sheets in Fig. 18(a).

Electrophoresis is now carried out simultaneously on both sheets in the indicated direction. At this pH, neutral peptides will not move (except by electro-osmosis), whereas basic (positively charged) peptides

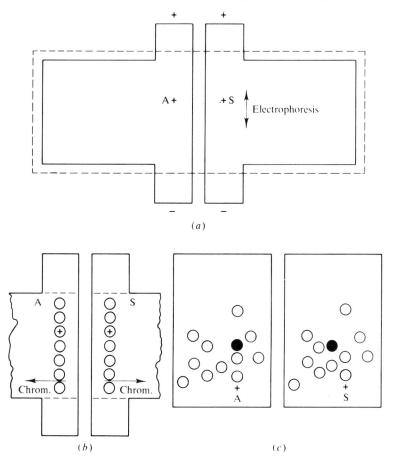

Figure 18. The three stages of peptide mapping or "fingerprinting."

will migrate toward the cathode and acidic peptides toward the anode. If the peptides were made visible by reaction with ninhydrin at the completion of the electrophoresis, the result would appear somewhat as in Fig. 18(b). Of course, the paper is not treated with ninhydrin at this point. Rather the tabs are cut off at the dotted lines in Fig. 18(b), and both are chromatographed simultaneously in the direction shown.

When the chromatography is complete, the two sheets are stained with ninhydrin to make visible the pattern or "fingerprint" [Fig. 18(c)]. The dissimilar peptides in these patterns have been marked on the figure by filling in the outlines of the spots. All other corresponding peptides have behaved identically. A photograph of the actual fingerprints of tryptic hydrolyzates of hemoglobins A and S as published by Ingram (1958) is shown in Fig. 19. The spots are not as ideally shaped as in Fig. 18, but the difference is apparent even though the photograph loses much in reproduction.

The results of this experiment confirmed that the difference in the proteins is restricted to a small portion of the polypeptide chain. In addition, the number of peptides on the fingerprint was an important item of information. The amino acid composition of hemoglobin as it was then known suggested the presence of about 60 lysyl and arginyl residues per 66,000 molecular weight. Because there are less than 30 spots on each pattern, it was concluded that the molecule is composed of identical halves, in agreement with x-ray diffraction data on the crystals. Hemoglobin A was then shown to have two pairs of chains (Rhinesmith, Schroeder, and Pauling, 1957), which have since been termed α and β chains. In conjunction with Ingram's fingerprints, this information limited the difference between hemoglobins A and S to some portion of one of the two types of chains. Ingram eluted the peptides from the fingerprints and detected a single difference in amino acid composition. The distinction between hemoglobins A and S, therefore, lay in a single residue in each of the two chains of one pair. By experiments that need not concern us here, the β chain was shown to be aberrant. After accumulated evidence had suggested that the alteration was near the N terminus, application of the Edman procedure proved that the N-terminal sequence of the β chains of hemoglobin A was Val-His-Leu-Thr-Pro-Glu- and that of hemoglobin S was Val-His-Leu-Thr-Pro-Val- (Shelton and Schroeder, 1960).

This information was obtained before much progress was made toward a determination of the complete sequence of hemoglobin. Because the difference was near the N terminus, the Edman procedure could be used with success. If the difference had been in some other portion of the chain, the precise point of change would have been more difficult to elucidate.

After the complete sequence of the α and β chains had been determined, the various peptides on the fingerprint could be correlated with their position in the sequence. At the present time, the point of aberration in an abnormal hemoglobin can be closely delimited if it can be associated with a particular peptide on the fingerprint.

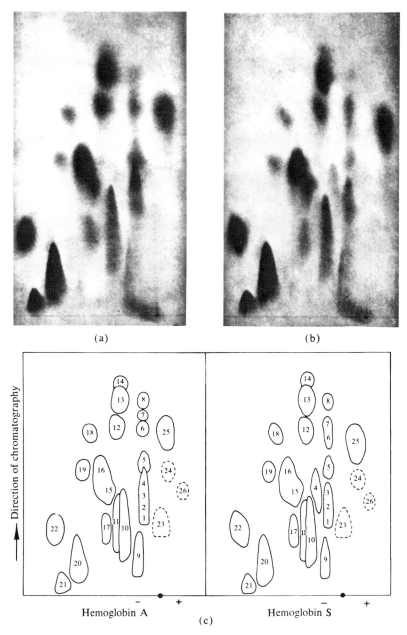

Figure 19. Fingerprints of hemoglobins A and S. a is from hemoglobin A, b is from hemoglobin S, and c is a tracing of the two. [Source: Ingram, *Biochem. Biophys. Acta*, **28**, 539 (1958).]

Aside from its value in the particular example that we are considering, fingerprinting in application to other proteins permits comparison
to be made and also gives an insight into the subunit structure of the
protein. Fingerprinting has thus proved itself to be a valuable tool.

Jones (1964) and co-workers (Benson *et al.*, 1966) have developed a
method of column fingerprinting that is even more sensitive than fingerprinting on paper. The principle of the automatic amino acid analyzer
has been applied to a mixture of peptides. Figure 20 depicts column
fingerprints of hemoglobins A and S. The difference is apparent.

Separation of Peptides from Hemoglobin

Let us now consider methods that were used for the isolation of
peptides from which the entire sequence of both chains of hemoglobin
A was deduced. Because this subject was actively investigated by three
groups, a variety of methods was used.

The point of unity in their methods lay in the chromatography on
ion-exchange resins with volatile developers. Braunitzer and co-workers
made use of the anion-exchange resin Dowex 1-X2. In various modifications of development, the column was equilibrated at some alkaline
pH with a buffer that contained two or three organic bases such as
pyridine, collidine, picoline, or lutidine with acetic acid to adjust the
pH. Gradient elution used a constant-volume mixer (Chapter 3, p. 19),
which was initially filled with the equilibrating developer and into
which stronger and stronger solutions of acetic acid were successively
passed stepwise. Figure 21 shows a separation of the tryptic peptides
of the normal β chain (Hilse and Braunitzer, 1962). In the lower
portion of the figure, the paper chromatographic examination of the peptides from the column indicates that many were heterogeneous. This
heterogeneity, therefore, required the application of a second method
to complete the separation. Braunitzer and co-workers chose to use
paper chromatography and paper electrophoresis for this purpose.

In their approach to the separation, Schroeder and co-workers
first chromatographed the mixture of tryptic peptides on Dowex 50-X2
with pyridine–acetic acid developers. The development involved a
gradient both in pH and pyridine concentration. Again this type of
chromatography failed to separate the mixture completely into individual peptides. In contrast to Braunitzer and colleagues, paper
methods were not used as the second stage of purification because of
the poor recovery of peptides from paper. Rather the second step
employed columns of Dowex 1-X2 in a manner similar to Braunitzer's.

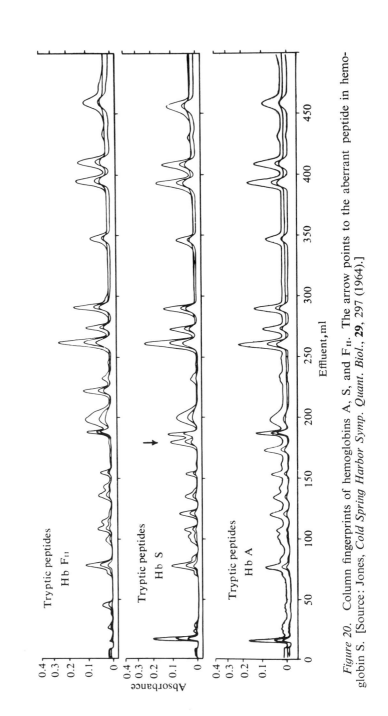

Figure 20. Column fingerprints of hemoglobins A, S, and F$_{\text{II}}$. The arrow points to the aberrant peptide in hemoglobin S. [Source: Jones, *Cold Spring Harbor Symp. Quant. Biol.*, **29**, 297 (1964).]

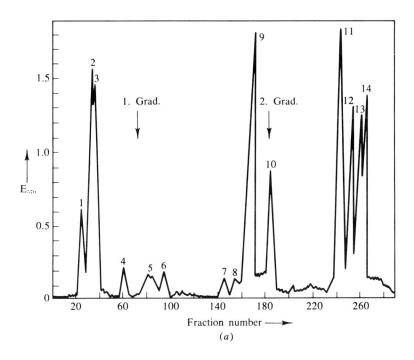

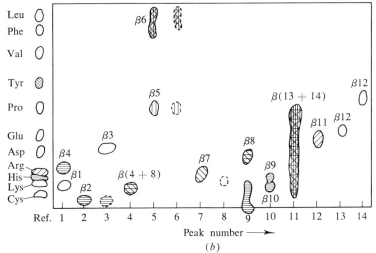

Figure 21. Separation of the tryptic peptides of the β chain of human hemoglobin A by column chromatography on Dowex 1. The examination of each zone by paper chromatography is depicted in the bottom part of the figure. [Source: Hilse and Braunitzer, *Z. physiol. Chem.*, **329**, 113 (1962).]

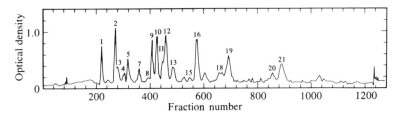

Figure 22. Separation of the tryptic peptides of the γ chain of human hemoglobin F by column chromatography on Dowex 50. [Source: Schroeder *et al.*, *Anal. Chem.*, **34**, 1570 (1962). Copyright 1962 by the American Chemical Society. Reprinted by permission of the copyright owner.]

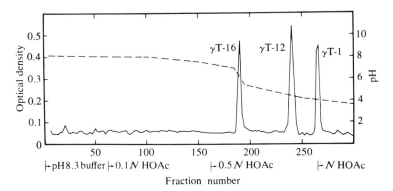

Figure 23. Separation of the peptides in Zone 12 of the chromatogram in Fig. 22 by chromatography on Dowex 1. [Source: Schroeder *et al.*, *Anal. Chem.*, **34**, 1570 (1962). Copyright 1962 by the American Chemical Society. Reprinted by permission of the copyright owner.]

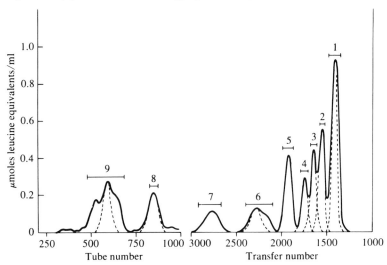

Figure 24. Separation of the soluble peptides of the α chain of human hemoglobin A by countercurrent distribution through 3057 transfers. [Source: Guidotti *et al.*, *J. Biol. Chem.*, **237**, 2184 (1962).]

A separation on Dowex 50 of tryptic peptides from the γ chain[1] of human fetal hemoglobin is depicted in Fig. 22 (Schroeder *et al.*, 1962). When the peptides in a zone equivalent to No. 12 in Fig. 22 were rechromatographed on Dowex 1, three peptides separated well (Fig. 23) despite their coincidence on Dowex 50.

Hill, Konigsberg, *et al.* employed countercurrent distribution (see Chapter 3, p. 30) in their initial separation of peptides in hemoglobin hydrolyzates. More than 3000 transfers were required to bring about the separation of peptides from the α chain of human hemoglobin as depicted in Fig. 24 from Guidotti, Hill, and Konigsberg (1962). The necessary further separations were achieved by chromatography on Dowex 50-X2; in this instance, pyridine–acetic acid developers in stepwise elution at several pH's and concentrations were used instead of gradient elution.

These examples illustrate well how varied are the approaches to peptide separations by different investigators.

GENERALIZATIONS AND APPROACHES TO PEPTIDE SEPARATIONS

An amino acid analysis requires only that a relatively simple mixture of limited composition be separated. In spite of the good chromatographic methods that were initially described to achieve this end, many variations and alterations have been published. On the other hand, when peptide mixtures are to be separated, no such simplicity prevails. The tryptic hydrolyzate of each protein is unique and is more or less complex. It is, therefore, hardly to be expected that any single procedure would suffice even if it would gain favor. We shall, in the rest of this chapter, discuss some factors that are important in peptide separations, describe some variations that have been used, and comment on some problems that must be faced. The emphasis will be on column chromatographic methods because almost every investigator of a protein of any complexity has been forced at some stage to use column methods. For specific details, the references of Chapter 14 should be examined. In that chapter, the sequences of many proteins are presented, and references to the experimental data are listed.

Preliminary Comments

In a determination of sequence, the method of separating the peptides is only a means to obtain a series of pure peptides. As a result,

---

[1] The γ chain in fetal hemoglobin is equivalent to the β chain in adult human hemoglobin. Both hemoglobins have identical α chains.

extensive investigation of methods for improving reasonable separations usually is not done. Each investigator alters conditions in the way in which experience has taught him to achieve a desired result. Except in the broadest sense, we yet know little about how a particular alteration in conditions will influence the behavior of a peptide until that change is tried. For example, acidic (negatively charged) peptides will *tend* to move rapidly on cation-exchange resins and to move slowly on anion-exchange resins. If a mixture of two acidic peptides will separate on a column of cation-exchange resin, the more rapidly moving one may be expected to emerge more slowly from a column of anion-exchange resin. However, we have no assurance of this result or, for that matter, of any separation on the anion exchanger because ionic character is not the sole determinant of chromatographic behavior.

It may be taken for granted that the peptides in the hydrolyzate of any complex protein usually will not be separated into pure individuals by any single procedure. Some basis for this statement is to be found in the example of hemoglobin that we have given above. Nevertheless, certain peptides whose isolation is depicted in Figs. 21, 22, and 24 showed little evidence of heterogeneity on further examination by chromatography or electrophoresis. However, if the peptide were analyzed after the first separation, the amounts of the amino acid residues frequently were not in the ratio of integral numbers. They became so only after purification by rechromatography, which showed little evidence of heterogeneity. At least a second stage of purification, therefore, is usually necessary to attain purity. Successful separation is most likely to be achieved when the second method is very dissimilar. We have seen this in Figs. 22 and 23 where the consecutive application of a cation and an anion exchanger resulted in an excellent separation.

The Chromatographic Support

For chromatography on ion-exchange resins, the materials of choice appear to be the strong cation and anion exchangers as represented by polystyrene lattices onto which are substituted sulfonic acid and quaternary ammonium groups, respectively. These are known by various commercial names such as Dowex 50 and Dowex 1[2] (Table 3, p. 18). Although the weak exchangers and the ion-exchange celluloses have been used, their application has been more specialized. The

---

[2] There is a tendency in the literature to combine all sulfonated polystyrene exchangers under the term "Dowex 50" and the quaternary ammonium derivatives under "Dowex 1." We shall do this also for simplicity.

success of the synthetic strong exchangers may well be due to reproducible characteristics from lot to lot or even from manufacturer to manufacturer and to their stability to vigorous procedures of regeneration which permit repeated usage. On the other hand, that a separation was successful only with a certain lot of an ion-exchange cellulose is often noted in the literature.

The degree of crosslinking as well as the type of ion-exchange resin must also be considered. In early separations of peptides on ion-exchange resins, it was reasoned that, because of their greater size as compared to amino acids, a more porous resin should be used. Whereas, therefore, Dowex 50-X8 (that is, 8 percent crosslinked resin) had been used for amino acid separations, Dowex 50-X2 became the common choice for peptide separations. Whether or not the reasoning was valid is not important, but it is certainly true that peptide separations under the same conditions of development are influenced by the degree of crosslinking. One can use successive chromatograms on columns of Dowex-50 with different degrees of crosslinking to complete the separation of a mixture in the same way as one might use Dowex 50 and then Dowex 1. There is a tendency toward the greater use of more highly crosslinked resins because of the higher dimensional stability. Because the 2 percent crosslinked resin shrinks and swells with change in ionic strength of the solvent, a chromatographic column usually must be repacked after the completion of a chromatogram. The 8 percent crosslinked resin changes inappreciably in size with ionic strength, and the column often can be reequilibrated to the original developer and used again without repouring.

The particle size of the resin is important. It is generally true that the smaller the particle size and the narrower the distribution of particle size the sharper will be the peak and the better the separation of similarly moving zones. Spherical or beaded resins of the Dowex 50-X8 type are now available with diameters of the order of 25μ. The physical properties of Dowex 50-X2 generally require fairly coarse sizes (greater than 200 mesh). Small particle size increases the resistance to solvent flow, but this disadvantage is overcome by using constant volume pumps that operate at pressures of several hundred pounds.

Size of Column

Columns of many sizes have been utilized for peptide separations. The choice is dependent to a large degree upon the quantity to be separated. Usually, the diameter is small in proportion to the length with ratios commonly 1 : 50 or more. At the lower end of size, dimensions such as 0.6 × 60 cm may be convenient but by no means the limit. Sizes such as 3 × 100 cm or 2 × 150 cm are frequently employed for initial separations of peptides in various hydrolyzates. The use of a 10 × 250-cm column has been reported; the sample was 21 g of hydrolyzate.

Size of Sample

The true capacity of an ion-exchange column has probably rarely been reached. Although a light load certainly does no harm, an increase in sample size usually does not noticeably worsen the separation. Furthermore, increasing the load rather than the size of the column permits the isolation of larger quantities of peptides without increasing the volume of solvents that must be removed. The hydrolyzate from 100 to 150 mg of protein is certainly a practical amount to use on a column with a cross-sectional area of 1 cm^2. On the other hand, it may be desirable in certain experiments to use as little as one mg per cm^2 of cross-sectional area. In general, quantities of a few micromoles of peptide may be conveniently handled on columns of the order of 0.6 × 60 cm.

Developers

The earliest attempts to apply ion-exchange columns to the separation of peptides used the same buffers that had been so successful in separating the amino acids. Many peptides were separated in this way. It was a major drawback that these buffers were 0.2M in sodium salts, which had to be removed before other examination of the peptide could be made. The problem was solved in several ways. In one instance, the peptides were converted to the DNP derivatives and extracted from the salt solution. Although successful for neutral and acidic peptides, the method was not applicable to basic peptides, and in addition the presence of the DNP group was a block to any degradative procedure. A more general method used ammonium salts in the developer. These salts could be sublimed in vacuo from the peptide and in fact had to be removed from individual fractions of the effluent before the ninhydrin procedure could be applied to assess the results of the chromatogram.

The use of volatile solvents marked a major advance. The components do not interfere with the application of the ninhydrin method. The evaporation of the solvents leaves a residue of peptide. As we have seen above, these volatile solvents usually use pyridine and methyl pyridines as the volatile bases; N-ethylmorpholine is another useful base. Formic and acetic acids are the acidic compounds. Different formulations are applicable to both anionic and cationic exchangers. For the former, development begins at high pH and for increasingly stronger development uses solvents of lower pH. For the latter, the reverse holds.

In some applications, developers with $8M$ urea and varying amounts of inorganic salts have been used. By means of Sephadex or Bio-Gel (Chapter 3, p. 21), which separate molecules on the basis of size, the recovery of the peptide from these contaminants[3] is a relatively simple operation.

In Chapter 3, various aspects of chromatographic development such as stepwise and gradient procedures have been described. The variety of developers is limited only by the imagination of the experimenter. Concentration and pH are the obvious variables. Steps of pH at constant concentration, of concentration at constant pH, or of both concentration and pH are used. These steps are reduced to infinitesimal size when gradients of many kinds are applied.

Flow Rate of Developer

As the capabilities of the methods have been explored, the time required to complete a chromatogram has decreased. Theoretically the smaller the ion-exchange particle the shorter is the time necessary for molecules of peptides and developers to diffuse in and out. The smaller the particle, therefore, the faster can be the flow rate. In some instances, flow rates of about 150 ml per cm^2 per hr have been used without apparent deterioration of the separation. In practice, such flow rates are most convenient with small columns. With large columns at such rates, the volumes of developer that emerge in a short time may become a burden to handle.

Detection of Peptides

The most widely used means of detecting a peptide in the effluent of a chromatogram is the ninhydrin method (Chapter 5, p. 48). Although amino acids with the exception of proline and hydroxyproline produce roughly equal amounts of color per mole with ninhydrin, peptides show a much greater variation and, if an N-terminal blocking group such as acetyl is present, they may produce almost no color. Consequently, it is common to apply alkaline hydrolysis prior to the

---

[3] Actually, the urea is an almost chemically pure solution with minor contamination by peptide.

reaction. This hydrolysis need not be quantitative. It is useful because it increases the sensitivity approximately as many times as there are residues in the peptide. These procedures can be automated.

As mentioned above, pyridine and similar bases in chromatographic developers do not interfere with the ninhydrin reaction. In fact, ammonia or substances that might give rise to it, such as urea, are really the only compounds to be avoided. In chromatograms where $8M$ urea has been used in the developer, spectrophotometric examination at 280 mμ will reveal at least those peptides that contain aromatic amino acids.

Recovery of Peptides

By "recovery of peptides" is meant the percentage that is regained from the effluent after a given amount has been chromatographed. This subject has not received much specific investigation. Data are usually presented in terms of the yield of peptide compared to that expected from a known amount of protein. Thus, if the tryptic hydrolyzate of 10 μmoles were chromatographed, 10 μmoles of each peptide would be expected. However, in most hydrolyzates a precipitate forms at some phase of the work and is removed before chromatography. Consequently, the actual amount of any peptide in the sample usually is known somewhat inaccurately. If one examines the literature, some peptides will be seen to have been isolated in yields that approach the quantitative, others are isolated to the extent of 20 percent or less, and still others do not emerge in a detectable way from a column at all. The higher yields are likely to be found among those peptides that emerge relatively rapidly from the column.

Gel Filtration

The basic principle of this method has been described in Chapter 3 (p. 21). A wide selection of materials is available for this procedure. The separation takes place largely on the basis of size. There is no real development in the ordinary sense, and any substance that can be dissolved will pass through in the same solvent. For this reason, the method is especially useful for the "insoluble" peptides that are usually met in some part of the determination of a sequence. Consider, for example, that it may be possible to dissolve a rather insoluble peptide and place it on an ion-exchange column. However, if the conditions of chromatography render it insoluble again, it may never be removed successfully from the column. With gel filtration materials such as

Bio-Gel and Sephadex, however, the entire separation may be carried out in 50 percent aqueous acetic acid or in buffered solutions of $8M$ urea in which most peptides are soluble. Although sharp separations are usually not achieved by this means, the method has been applied with considerable success in many instances.

PEPTIDE SEPARATIONS ON PAPER AND THIN LAYERS

Many factors discussed above for column chromatograms are not applicable to paper or thin-layer chromatography or electrophoresis. On the other hand, paper or thin-layer techniques would seem to be necessary for "diagonal" methods, which will be mentioned in another connection (Chapter 13, p. 164).

With paper techniques, one is limited to a single support whose properties to a degree may be altered by coating with various substances prior to chromatography. For example, if paper is dipped in an acetone solution of a relatively nonvolatile liquid such as formamide and the acetone is allowed to evaporate, the formamide will coat the paper and the chromatographic properties will differ from those of untreated paper. If one turns to ion-exchange papers, an entirely different set of conditions apply, and the support can hardly be considered a variant of paper.

Thin-layer chromatography lends itself to the use of a wide variety of organic and inorganic substances. In many ways, it is a geometrically different form of column chromatography. It has not yet had wide application to peptide separations.

Limitation in the amount of sample that can be chromatographed is a very real disadvantage of paper chromatography in peptide separations in which sufficient material for further examination usually is the goal. This difficulty can be overcome to a degree by using a wide paper and by applying the sample in a long stripe. After development, the stripes of separated peptides can be cut out, sewed to another sheet, and developed with another solvent. Obviously, this process can be repeated. Thin-layer methods, in general, appear to have a much greater capacity than paper methods.

Stepwise development is rarely applied in paper chromatography. The developers that may be chosen, however, are almost innumerable in their variety: many ingenious combinations of pH and of aqueous and organic mixtures have been used. Development with an electric potential—electrophoresis—must not be forgotten. Here the charge is an important factor and can of course be altered by changing the pH.

Large quantities may be isolated by electrophoretic means if the "hanging curtain" type of apparatus is used.

General detection of peptides on paper or thin layers is commonly achieved with ninhydrin. The possibility of applying successively reagents that are specific for certain amino acids (arginine, histidine, tryptophan, etc.) is a real advantage of paper and thin-layer methods. Much information is thus quickly obtained.

It is difficult to recover peptides in good yield from paper. Losses of 50 to 75 percent for each chromatogram are not uncommon.

COMMENTS

The state of affairs in methods of peptide separation is good. Many choices of procedure are available, and any combination of methods may be (and probably has been) used. A major problem that remains at the present time is the purification of large, relatively insoluble peptides. Gel filtration is a help, but a new generally applicable procedure would facilitate sequence determinations.

REFERENCES

BENSON, J. V., JR., R. T. JONES, J. CORMICK, AND J. A. PATTERSON (1966), Accelerated Automatic Chromatographic Analysis of Peptides on a Spherical Resin, *Anal. Biochem.*, **16**, 91.

CONSDEN, R., A. H. GORDON, AND A. J. P. MARTIN (1944), Qualitative Analysis of Proteins: a Partition Chromatographic Method Using Paper, *Biochem. J.*, **38**, 224.

GUIDOTTI, G., R. J. HILL, AND W. KONIGSBERG (1962), The Structure of Human Hemoglobin. II. The Separation and Amino Acid Composition of the Tryptic Peptides from the α and β Chains, *J. Biol. Chem.*, **237**, 2184.

HILSE, K., AND G. BRAUNITZER (1962), Über Hämoglobine, IX. Isolierung und Charakterisierung der tryptischen Spaltprodukte des normalen adulten Humanhämoglobins, *Z. physiol. Chem.*, **329**, 113.

INGRAM, V. M. (1956), A Specific Chemical Difference between the Globins of Normal Human and Sickle-cell Anaemia Haemoglobin, *Nature*, **178**, 792.

INGRAM, V. M. (1958), Abnormal Human Haemoglobins. I. The Comparison of Normal Human and Sickle-cell Haemoglobins by "Fingerprinting," *Biochim. Biophys. Acta*, **28**, 539.

JONES, R. T. (1964), Structural Studies of Aminoethylated Hemoglobins by Automatic Peptide Chromatography, *Cold Spring Harbor Symp. Quant. Biol.*, **29**, 297.

PAULING, L., H. A. ITANO, S. J. SINGER, AND I. C. WELLS (1949), Sickle Cell
   Anemia, a Molecular Disease, *Science*, **110**, 543.
RHINESMITH, H. S., W. A. SCHROEDER, AND L. PAULING (1957), A Quantitative
   Study of the Hydrolysis of Human Dinitrophenyl (DNP) globin: The
   Number and Kind of Polypeptide Chains in Normal Adult Human
   Hemoglobin, *J. Am. Chem. Soc.*, **79**, 4682.
SCHROEDER, W. A., R. T. JONES, J. CORMICK, AND K. MC CALLA (1962), Chromato-
   graphic Separation of Peptides on Ion Exchange Resins. Separation of
   Peptides from Enzymatic Hydrolyzates of the α, β, and γ Chains of
   Human Hemoglobins, *Anal. Chem.*, **34**, 1570.
SHELTON, J. R., AND W. A. SCHROEDER (1960), Further N-Terminal Sequences
   in Human Hemoglobins A, S, and F by Edman's Phenylthiohydantoin
   Method, *J. Am. Chem. Soc.*, **82**, 3342.

11

SEQUENCE DETERMINATION
IN PEPTIDES

After peptides have been successfully isolated from one or another hydrolyzate, the next step is to establish the composition and sequence of the individual peptides. The whole process begins again in miniature: analysis, N-terminal determination, sequential degradation followed often by further hydrolysis, etc.

When a peptide has been isolated, the problem of its homogeneity remains. Usually, two stages of purification are necessary, but more may be required. If two types of column chromatography have been used for the initial isolation, many workers test purity by submitting a portion of the peptide to paper electrophoresis and/or chromatography. If no heterogeneity is apparent, further examination can be made with confidence. If an analysis shows that the amino acids are present in the ratio of small integral numbers, the next criterion has been met. The analytical data, however, can be a valuable guide to further investigation.

AMINO ACID ANALYSIS

The amino acid analysis of a peptide allows us to deduce much about future problems and possibilities in determining its sequence. An analysis is such a simple procedure now that it is warranted whenever there is reasonable evidence of purity. An examination by paper methods may even be dispensed with because the analysis will be equally indicative.

Examination of Data

In Table 8, the analytical results from three peptides of the author's experience are given. For each peptide, the analysis in terms of μmoles

 References for Chapter 11, pp. 153–154.

TABLE 8. *The Amino Acid Analyses of Three Peptides*

Amino Acid	Peptide 1[a]		Peptide 2[b]		Peptide 3[c]	
	μ moles	Residues	μ moles	Residues	μ moles	Residues
Lys	0.195	2.03	0.119	**2.25**		
His			0.004	0.08		?
Arg	0.096	1.00	0.008	0.15		
Asp	0.378	3.94	0.053	**1.00**	0 022	
Thr	0.269	2.80	0.009	0.17	0.410	
Ser	0.099	1.03	0.019	0.36	0.165	
Glu	0.095	0.99	0.013	0.25	0.280	
Pro	0.305	3.18				
Gly	0.469	4.89	0.060	**1.13**	0.028	
Ala	0.186	1.94	0.096	**1.81**	0.462	
Val	0.284	2.96	0.054	**1.02**	0.800	
Met						
Ile					0.016	
Leu	0.287	2.99	0.095	**1.79**	0.966	
Tyr						
Phe						

[a] Peptide 1. Ala-Ala-Gln-Lys-Pro-Asp-Val-Leu-Thr-Thr-Gly-Gly-Gly-Asn-Pro-Val-Gly-Asp-Lys-Leu-Asn-Ser-Leu-Thr-Val-Gly-Pro-Arg.

[b] Peptide 2. Gly-Lys-Lys-Val-Ala-Asp-Ala-Leu.

[c] Peptide 3. 45 percent of Val-Thr-Val-Leu; 30 percent of Ala-Gln-Leu; 21 percent of Ser-Ala-Leu; and 3 percent of Gly-Asn-Leu.

is shown in one column and in number of residues of each amino acid in the adjoining column. Because a known weight of peptide is rarely analyzed, all that can be or need be deduced is the integral number of residues of each amino acid in the peptide.

A cursory glance at the data for Peptide 1 shows a variety of quantities and suggests a mixture. Yet on careful examination it is seen that arginine, serine, and glutamic acid are in equal amount. If, then, a quantity of 0.096 μmoles is assumed to be indicative of a single residue of amino acid and all μmolar quantities are divided by this number, the resulting residues in the adjacent column fall within 6 percent of an integral number. This analysis of a 28-residue peptide for which the sequence is given below the table is excellent and was completely substantiated by the determination of the sequence.

The analysis of Peptide 2 is rather different. If the smallest amount is used to calculate the number of residues, the results are absurd. Consequently, the smaller amounts must be considered to be impurities, and a more reasonable basis must be chosen by inspection. If 0.053 μmoles is used, the adjacent numbers result. These are by no means as close to integral numbers as in the first example. However, this is an interpretable analysis, and it may be concluded with reasonable assurance that the numbers in bold face type when reduced to the nearest integer represent the amino acid composition of the main peptide. This, indeed, proved to be so as the sequence below Table 8 shows. Nevertheless, at this stage, the peptide was contaminated with other peptide(s) to a considerable degree.

The analysis of Peptide 3 in many ways resembles that of Peptide 2. Nevertheless, it was not possible to unscramble these data, because a quaternary mixture of small peptides was present in the proportions listed at the bottom of Table 8. Further separation was required before the sequences of these peptides could be determined. If only two peptides are present and especially if the amounts are unequal, it is often possible to deduce the amino acid composition of both with considerable confidence.

Deductions from the Amino Acid Composition

The amino acid analysis of the peptide gives immediate information about its size, which may range from a single amino acid to a length much greater than the 28-residue peptide of Table 8.

The analysis in combination with other information permits several conclusions to be drawn and provides a basis for planning future experiments to elucidate the sequence completely. Suppose, for example, that the peptide under consideration derived from a tryptic hydrolyzate as did Peptide 1 of Table 8. On the basis of the specificity of trypsin, lysine or arginine in the peptide would be C-terminal. Of course, in this example, two lysyl and one arginyl residues are present and only one can be C-terminal. The presence of three basic residues, then, in itself is evidence of sequences that prevent the usual cleavage. This deduction is borne out by the final sequence because -Lys-Pro- is never hydrolyzed by trypsin and the proximity of aspartic acid to the -Lys-Leu- bond reduces the rate of cleavage. If the analysis of a tryptic peptide fails to reveal either arginine or lysine, the peptide potentially derives from the C terminus of the chain; however, one cannot at this point exclude the possibility of an abnormal hydrolysis by trypsin.

Peptide 1 is a long peptide for which further partial hydrolysis is likely to be necessary before the complete sequence can be elucidated. The amino acid composition gives a hint of possible points for further cleavage. The three leucyl residues presumably could be cleaved by chymotrypsin, but phenylalanyl and tyrosyl residues, which are also susceptible to this enzyme, are absent. At this point in the study, the presence of four aspartyl residues suggests the possibility of cleavage with acetic acid (Chapter 9, p. 108) although, if all were in the form of asparagine, cleavage would be minimal.

With the knowledge that Peptide 2 of Table 8 was from a chymotryptic hydrolyzate, similar examination of the data may be made.

APPLICATION OF THE EDMAN PROCEDURE TO PEPTIDES

The chemistry of the Edman PTH method has been discussed in Chapter 6 (p. 74). The procedure is valuable in identifying N-terminal amino acids in the protein and in showing the sequence of a few residues near the N terminus. By far its greatest usefulness has been in its application to peptides. Without it, the determination of the sequence of a protein would be far more difficult. Once a pure peptide has been isolated and analyzed, the Edman method is no doubt the next procedure that should be applied. However, because there are problems associated with the application of the Edman method, many modifications have been described. Some of the more important will now be discussed.

The Edman Method on Paper Strips

In some of the first applications to proteins, the insolubility of the product at certain steps of the Edman procedure seriously limited its usefulness. To overcome this problem, Fraenkel-Conrat (Fraenkel-Conrat *et al.*, 1955) devised a modification in which the material to be degraded was absorbed on paper strips, and all reactions and extractions were carried out on this medium. Although this modification in its original form is not applicable to peptides because of the *solubility* of derivatives at various stages, further alteration of conditions (Schroeder *et al.*, 1963a) has made it satisfactory for peptides. A brief description follows.

A solution of peptide is absorbed on several 1 × 7-cm strips of filter paper. After the solvent has evaporated, the strips are wet with a solution of phenylisothiocyanate in dioxane and kept in a closed vessel at 40°C in the vapors above a solution of pyridine, dioxane, and water for 3 hr. Excess reagents are removed by repeated extraction with benzene over a period of several hours. After the strips have been dried in air, they are suspended in the vapors of glacial acetic acid and 6N hydrochloric acid at a pressure of 100 torr. The cyclization and

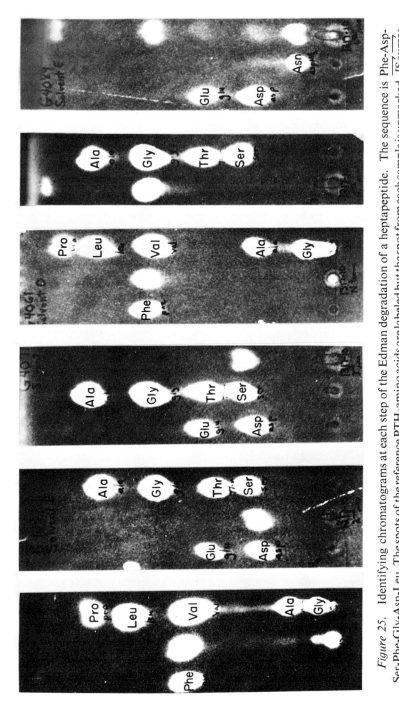

Figure 25. Identifying chromatograms at each step of the Edman degradation of a heptapeptide. The sequence is Phe-Asp-Ser-Phe-Gly-Asn-Leu. The spots of the reference PTH-amino acids are labeled but the spot from each sample is unmarked. [Source: Schroeder *et al.*, *Biochemistry*, **2**, 992 (1963). Copyright 1963 by the American Chemical Society. Reprinted by permission of the copyright owner.]

removal of the N-terminal amino acid takes place under these conditions in the course of some hours at room temperature. Following this step, the PTH-amino acid is extracted with acetone from the thoroughly dried strips. The strips, after drying, are ready for the next degradation. The PTH-amino acid in the acetone extract may readily be identified by paper chromatography in systems described by Sjöquist (1953) and Edman and Sjöquist (1956). Figure 25 is representative of the results that may be obtained when a peptide is taken through a number of degradations. The last of at least two chromatograms that are required for identification is shown. The PTH-amino acid that is removed at each step is positively identified. The identification of phenylalanine is unequivocal because valine is absent from the peptide. Leucine is placed by difference. As can be seen, traces of PTH-amino acid representative of the preceding step are usually apparent.

Although a convenient schedule for this particular procedure allows a degradation to be begun every other day, the actual effort expended during this period is small and a dozen degradations can be under way simultaneously. It is possible to identify serine, threonine, asparagine, and glutamine by this method although as will be noted below these amino acids can be troublesome in other procedures; however, histidine presents some problems. The paper strip method is especially susceptible to oxidizing atmospheric pollutants (smog) and requires special precautions. The number of successful degradations that may be carried out on any given peptide is dependent on the individual peptide and can be determined only by trial.

The Edman Method in Solution

The Edman method in solution has many modifications, which involve the type of base for pH control during the reaction with phenylisothiocyanate, the solvent for extracting excess reagents, the acid for the cyclization, etc. In many instances, solution methods are used "subtractively," that is, the peptide is first analyzed, then degraded, and analyzed again. The difference in the analyses determines which amino acid has been removed by the degradation.

The procedure of Konigsberg and Hill (1962) to be described now, although typical of many subtractive modifications in solution, introduces a chromatographic purification at each step. The analyzed peptide is allowed to react with phenylisothiocyanate in a buffer of N-ethylmorpholine, acetic acid, and ethanol at 37°C for 2.5 hr. After the solvents have been evaporated, the dry residue is extracted with benzene, dried, and treated with anhydrous trifluoroacetic acid at room temperature for

1 hr in order to bring about the cyclization. The solvent is removed again, the residue is dissolved in aqueous acetic acid, and the solution is extracted with benzene. The aqueous phase is finally chromato-graphed on a small column (0.3 × 6 cm) of Dowex 50-X2 with several developers, and a portion of the degraded peptide so isolated is analyzed to determine which amino acid has been removed. The remainder is ready for another degradation.

The results of an application of this procedure are presented in Table 9. Although the removal at each step is not quantitative, the type of residue that has been removed is apparent.

TABLE 9.   *Results of the Degradation of a Hexapeptide by an Edman Method in Solution*

Degra-dation no.	Amino acid[a]				
	Alanine	*Histidine*	*Glycine*	*Glutamic acid*	*Tyrosine*
0[b]	2.03	1.04	1.05	0.98	0.94
1	**0.89**[c]	0.83	0.87	1.00	1.11
2	1.17	**0.05**	1.20	0.90	0.79
3	**0.16**	0.05	1.31	0.92	0.72
4	0.15	0.00	**0.28**	1.00	0.68
5	0.10	0.00	0.29	**0.16**	1.00

The sequence: Ala-His-Ala-Gly-Glu-Tyr

[a] The data are in terms of residues of each amino acid.

[b] This is the composition of the original peptide.

[c] The numbers in bold face type identify the type of residue that is less than in the preceding analysis and has been removed by the degradation.

SOURCE: Konigsberg and Hill, *J. Biol. Chem.*, **237**, 2547 (1962).

As mentioned above, a subtractive procedure cannot distinguish between aspartic acid and asparagine or between glutamic acid and gluta-mine because only the acids appear in the complete hydrolyzate. If a solution method is used with positive identification of the PTH-amino acid at each step, it is frequently difficult to determine PTH-serine or PTH-threonine. This type of procedure has had widespread use in sequence determinations despite the fact that an amino acid analysis is required at each step.

The Edman Method on a Solid Support

A modification of the Edman procedure that is still in the process of development uses a solid insoluble isothiocyanate (Stark, 1965). The solid isothiocyanate is formed on styrene that has been polymerized with 0.5 percent divinylbenzene to give a preparation equivalent to unsulfonated Dowex 50-X0.5. The polymer is carried through a series of reactions, where R is the polystyrene lattice:

$$\text{Polymer} \quad + \quad HNO_3 \quad \longrightarrow \quad \underset{NO_2}{\overset{R}{\bigcirc}} \quad + \quad SnCl_2 \quad \longrightarrow$$

$$\underset{NH_2}{\overset{R}{\bigcirc}} \quad + \quad CSCl_2 \quad \longrightarrow \quad \underset{NCS}{\overset{R}{\bigcirc}}$$

In the procedure, the polymer isothiocyanate is formed into a column, and the peptide in solution is absorbed into the column and allowed to react at room temperature for 15 min. At the end of this time, any unreacted peptide is washed from the column. Anhydrous trifluoroacetic acid brings about the cyclization. Insoluble thiohydantoin amino acid remains behind on washing the column, whereas the degraded peptide is present in the effluent. The procedure must be used "subtractively."

This method presumably has the advantage of self-purification of the products at several stages. Thus, after the initial reaction any unreacted material is removed, whereas after cyclization any uncyclized material remains behind and does not contaminate the degraded peptide. At the present time, a number of technical difficulties prevent the successful application of the method to all peptides.

In a somewhat similar way, Laursen (1966) has devised a procedure in which the peptide is attached to the resin through a carboxyl group and remains fixed through the successive degradations.

The Edman Method and the Dansyl Method

The Edman method in conjunction with the dansyl procedure (Chapter 6, p. 77) may be termed a "positive "subtractive procedure. It has been applied by Gray and Hartley (1963) in the following way. After the N-terminal residue has been identified with a portion of the peptide by the dansyl method, the remainder is degraded by an Edman method in solution. A portion of degraded peptide is used to identify the second residue, and the remainder is degraded again. The dansyl procedure thus identifies each new residue as it is exposed through the Edman degradation.

The method has the advantage of a positive identification at each step and, in addition, may be used with small quantities because of the sensitivity of the dansyl procedure. It should be noted that the method is only as good as the Edman procedure that is applied.

Comments

Despite the many modifications that have been proposed for the Edman degradation, none is without its problems. Although the yields at each step are generally good (80 percent or better) for most procedures, there are side reactions of unknown nature that sometimes reduce yields rather drastically. The automatic Edman procedure (pp. 75 and 90) is not easily applicable to small peptides because of their solubility in the solvents. However, the information that Edman has obtained in his careful study of all phases of the procedure may make it possible to improve the manual methods.

The degradation cannot be applied if a blocked N-terminal group is present or if a pyrrolidone carboxylic acid residue has formed by the cyclization of N-terminal glutamine (p. 79). Despite limitations, the Edman degradation is essential in present-day sequence work. It may be expected to yield information about the first to the tenth residues in a peptide depending upon unknown factors. In any event, this method is the first procedure to apply after a peptide has been analyzed and is judged to be pure.

FURTHER STEPS FOR DETERMINING THE SEQUENCE OF PEPTIDES

The question may be asked, "If the Edman fails and the sequence of the peptide is incomplete, then what?" At this point information from the Edman procedure, from the amino acid composition, and from the charge on the peptide must be carefully evaluated. The main question to be answered is whether there are potential points of enzymatic or chemical cleavage. If there are, the peptide may be broken into smaller pieces and each in turn can be isolated, analyzed, and degraded.

Suppose that examination by the Edman technique had established the partial structure of a neutral tryptic peptide as

Leu-Ala-Gly-(Asp, Pro, Val, Gly, Ala)-Lys

in which lysine is placed on the basis of the specificity of trypsin.

These results speak against the use of chymotrypsin, because the removal of leucine would not substantially alter the peptide. On the other hand, if one of the residues within the parentheses were phenylalanyl, the possibility of a useful cleavage by chymotrypsin is increased although this possibility would not be realized if a -Phe-Pro- sequence were present. Needless to say, enzymatic hydrolysis is not limited to trypsin and chymotrypsin. Excellent and useful cleavages may often be obtained by enzymes of broad specificity such as papain, pepsin, or subtilopeptidase.

The specificity of the enzyme leucine aminopeptidase (LAP) can be of great use in completing the sequence of a peptide. LAP releases amino acids that have a free α-amino group by acting upon the connecting peptide bond[1], but it will not hydrolyze a peptide bond that involves proline:

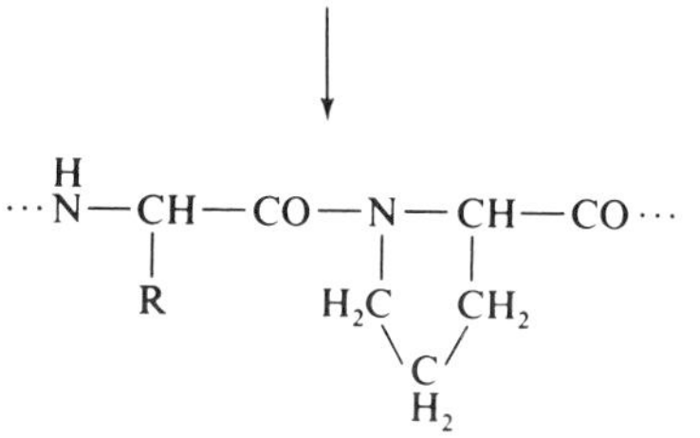

$$\cdots N{-}CH{-}CO{-}N{-}CH{-}CO\cdots$$

Consequently, when LAP is allowed to act on a peptide, free amino acids are successively released, but if proline is present, the action stops at the peptide bond N-terminal to the imide bond. The resulting peptide contains the residue on the N-terminal side of the proline as well as proline and those C-terminal to it. Thus, if the peptide in the above illustration has the sequence of amino acids shown within the parentheses, the action of LAP would cease after the release of leucine, alanine, and glycine, and the peptide (Asp, Pro, Val, Gly, Ala)-Lys would remain. By isolating it and applying the Edman procedure, the entire sequence of the peptide might be elucidated. If the rate of release of amino acids is followed, LAP may be and has been used for determining the sequence of a few amino acids. In like manner, carboxypeptidase has been used to identify short sequences at the C terminus of peptides.

The specificity of LAP may be valuable occasionally, even if proline is absent. This occurs when the peptide contains aspartic acid. Suppose

---

[1] It, therefore, acts from the N terminus in contrast to carboxypeptidase.

that the proline in our illustrative peptide were isoleucine, and the peptide were Leu-Ala-Gly-Asp-Ile-Val-Gly-Ala-Lys. An acid hydrolysis would yield the composition (Asp_1, Gly_2, Ala_2, Val_1, Ile_1, Leu_1, Lys_1). If proline is absent, LAP itself is an excellent means of hydrolyzing a peptide to determine its amino acid composition. Yet if this were done, the composition from the LAP hydrolyzate would probably be ($Asp_{0.5}$, $Gly_{1.5}$, $Ala_{1.5}$, $Val_{0.5}$, $Ile_{0.5}$, Leu_1, $Lys_{0.5}$). Those residues that are present in only half the expected amount are aspartic acid and all residues C-terminal to it. This behavior of aspartic acid is a result of a partial shift of the peptide bond from the α to the β carboxyl group in this way:

$$
\begin{array}{ccc}
\text{H} & \text{H} & \text{H} \\
\cdots\text{N—CHR—CO—N—CH—CO—N—CHR}'\text{—CO}\cdots \rightleftharpoons \\
\text{|} \\
\text{CH}_2\text{—COOH}
\end{array}
$$

α form

$$
\begin{array}{cc}
\text{H} & \text{H} \\
\cdots\text{N—CHR—CO—N—CH—COOH} \\
\text{|} \qquad\qquad \text{H} \\
\text{CH}_2\text{—CO—N—CHR}'\text{—CO}\cdots
\end{array}
$$

β form

Because LAP will not hydrolyze the β form, aspartic acid and residues C-terminal to it are released only from those molecules in the α form. The position of an aspartyl residue can be deduced in this way. This α to β rearrangement of aspartic acid has been studied in some detail by Naughton et al. (1960): it no doubt occurs during the isolation of the peptide.

If our model peptide contains an aspartyl rather than an asparaginyl residue, it is a candidate for cleavage with acetic acid (Chapter 9, p. 108). It has been stated above that the peptide was neutral.[2] Consequently, an aspartyl residue must be present, because only in this way could compensation by made for the positive charge of the lysyl residue. Refluxing in acetic acid should yield Leu-Ala-Gly, free aspartic acid, and (Pro, Val, Gly, Ala)-Lys. This is a simple procedure that often can be used to good advantage.

In our example, the charge of the peptide is a ready indicator of the presence of an aspartyl rather than an asparaginyl residue. When a

---

[2] Paper electrophoresis at neutral pH is a convenient procedure for ascertaining the charge of a peptide. Chromatographic behavior especially on Dowex 1 also is frequently indicative.

peptide by analysis contains more than one acidic amino acid, the charge may be of equivocal help in detecting the presence or absence of amide groups. For example, if a neutral peptide contained aspartic acid, glutamic acid, and lysine by analysis, either asparagine or glutamine must be present, but charge alone cannot distinguish between them. It may be difficult to ascertain the position of amide groups in a peptide. As noted above, most PTH procedures do not permit this identification. Although analysis of LAP hydrolyzates can be of great assistance, the problem is often resolved by breaking the peptide into such small peptides that the charge is definitive.

A procedure of Ressler and Kashelikar (1966) may prove to be of value for identifying asparaginyl and glutaminyl residues. The following series of reactions has been used:

$$\cdots \underset{\substack{| \\ (CH_2)_n-CONH_2}}{\overset{H}{N}}-CH-CO-\underset{}{\overset{H}{N}}\cdots \xrightarrow[\text{chlorophosphite}]{\text{ethylene}} \cdots \underset{\substack{| \\ (CH_2)_n-C\equiv N}}{\overset{H}{N}}-CH-CO-\underset{}{\overset{H}{N}}\cdots \xrightarrow[\text{CH}_3\text{OH}]{\text{Na, NH}_3} \cdots \underset{\substack{| \\ (CH_2)_n-CH_2-NH_2}}{\overset{H}{N}}-CH-CO-\underset{}{\overset{H}{N}}\cdots$$

In a hydrolyzate of the reduction product, diaminobutyric acid will have derived from asparagine and ornithine from glutamine. Both may be estimated by automatic amino acid analysis. If a prolyl residue were C-terminal to the asparaginyl or glutaminyl residue, reduction with sodium in ammonia might invalidate the results (see p. 113).

If a peptide has a methionyl residue, cleavage with cyanogen bromide can be applied. This excellent method is of limited value because of the relatively small number of methionyl residues in most proteins.

MASS SPECTROMETRY

Mass spectrometry has been applied with success to the elucidation of the structure of several naturally occurring lipopeptides.

The method requires that the sample be fragmented in an electron beam at high vacuum. The positive ions are accelerated toward a negative electrode through a collimating system into a magnetic field where they are sorted according to charge to mass ratio. High resolution mass spectrometry is able to determine masses to ± 1 millimass unit. Such high resolution actually allows elementary compositions to be calculated with considerable confidence. The reader is referred to Biemann (1962), McLafferty (1966), Shemyakin et al. (1966), and other books for a detailed discussion of mass spectrometry and its application to the identification of peptides.

When mass spectrometry is applied to a peptide, the major fragmentation occurs at the peptide bond. As a result, one obtains as the main fragments a series of charged particles that correspond to the original peptide as well as to other peptides in which a residue at a time has been cleaved. For example, Bricas *et al.* (1965) have examined acyl methyl esters of Ala-Val-Gly-Leu. The positive ions corresponding to

$$RCO\text{-}Ala\text{-}Val\text{-}Gly\text{-}Leu\text{-}OCH_3,$$
$$Ala\text{-}Val\text{-}Gly\text{-}Leu\text{-}OCH_3,$$
$$Val\text{-}Gly\text{-}Leu\text{-}OCH_3,$$
$$Gly\text{-}Leu\text{-}OCH_3,$$
$$\text{and } Leu\text{-}OCH_3$$

were the most important in deducing a structure. These fragments, of course, were not the only ones that were apparent on the mass spectrogram. The very complexity of the spectrum requires computer techniques for its evaluation.

One requirement of mass spectrometry, which is perhaps the most difficult to meet with peptides, is volatility. The peptide must be sufficiently volatile so that the molecules may reach the electron beam to be fragmented. Normally, peptides are very involatile because of their dipolar ionic character. The method has been most successful with acylated peptide esters as we have seen in the above example. An application to a naturally occurring eicosanoyl nonapeptide ester called fortuitine was successful in determining its sequence (Barber *et al.*, 1965).

Mass spectrometry requires minute amounts of the order of micrograms. The actual determination of the spectrum requires little time, and its assessment can be done rapidly by computer. Potentially, it is a valuable tool for studying peptides. How useful it will be remains to be tested.

EXAMPLES OF SEQUENCE DETERMINATION IN SEVERAL TYPICAL PEPTIDES

Before concluding this discussion of methods for determining the sequence of amino acids in peptides, we shall present examples to show how some of the methods have been applied to actual peptides.

A Peptide from Catalase

From a tryptic hydrolyzate of catalase (Schroeder *et al.*, 1964), a peptide with the amino acid composition (His, Arg, Asp, Thr$_2$, Glu,

Gly$_3$, Ala$_2$, Val, Ile, Tyr, Phe$_2$) was isolated. The Edman degradation established the partial sequence as

Gly-Ala-Gly-Ala-(His, Asp, Thr$_2$, Glu, Gly, Val, Ile, Tyr, Phe$_2$)-Arg.
→ → → →

The arrow under each abbreviation depicts the result of consecutive successful applications of the Edman degradation. Arginine is placed at the C terminus on the basis of the specificity of trypsin. There are many potential points for chymotryptic cleavage in this peptide, and its application resulted in an almost ideal splitting into four peptides of which the structures were

(1) Gly-Ala-Gly-Ala-Phe
→ → → →

(2) Gly-Tyr-Phe
→ →

(3) Glu-Val-Thr-His
→ → → →

(4) Asp-Ile-Thr-Arg.
→ → → →

Note that the potential cleavage between tyrosine and phenylalanine did not occur whereas that at histidine did.

Peptide 1 obviously derives from the N terminus and peptide 4 from the C terminus, but the relation of peptides 2 and 3 to 1 and 4 remains to be determined. In this case, the chymotryptic hydrolysis of catalase itself had yielded a peptide (His, Arg, Asp, Thr$_2$, Glu, Val, Ile, Tyr), which upon Edman degradation showed the sequence Glu-Val-Thr-His-Asp-Ile-Thr-Arg-Tyr. This sequence matches those of peptides 3 and 4 and permits the entire sequence of the original peptide to be written as Gly-Ala-Gly-Ala-Phe-Gly-Tyr-Phe-Glu-Val-Thr-His-Asp-Ile-Thr-Arg.

Another Peptide from Catalase

A chymotryptic hydrolyzate of catalase contained a neutral peptide with the amino acid composition (Lys, Asp$_2$, Thr$_2$, Pro, Gly$_4$, Val, Leu) (Schroeder *et al.*, 1964). The Edman degradation allowed a partial structure to be written as

Thr-Thr-Gly-Gly-Gly-(Lys, Asp$_2$, Pro, Gly, Val)-Leu.
→ → → → →

(The leucine is tentatively placed at the C terminus on the basis of the specificity of chymotrypsin.) One is justified in viewing such results with some skepticism because of the repeating sequences. If the degradation of a particular residue has not been entirely satisfactory, the same type of residue may be evident at the succeeding degradation and simulate a repeating sequence. Thus, when the same type of residue appears in succession, a good yield is necessary in both steps to ensure that the same residue is indeed present.[3]

The presence of proline in this peptide suggested the application of LAP. When a small portion was treated with LAP and submitted directly to amino acid analysis, free threonine and glycine in the ratio of 2 to 3 substantiated the results of the Edman degradation. The part of the peptide unhydrolyzed by LAP had the sequence Asn-Pro-Val-Gly-Asp-Lys-Leu. All residues of the original chymotryptic peptide can, therefore, be placed in sequence.

A Peptide from the α Chain of Human Hemoglobin

A tryptic hexadecapeptide from the human α chain has the amino acid composition (Lys, His$_2$, Asp, Thr, Ser$_2$, Glu, Pro, Gly, Ala, Val, Leu, Tyr, Phe$_2$). The scheme that Konigsberg and Hill (1962) employed to establish the sequence of this peptide is presented in Fig. 26. The

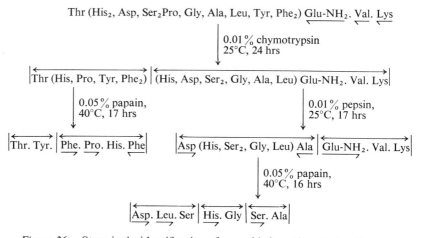

Figure 26.   Steps in the identification of a peptide from the α chain of human hemoglobin A. [Source: Konigsberg and Hill, *J. Biol. Chem.*, **237**, 2547 (1962).]

[3] Because the paper strip modification with positive identification of the removed residue was used in this example, the yield of PTH-amino acid is important. In a subtractive procedure, one would look for the disappearance of residues in almost quantitative amount.

approach to the determination is somewhat different than that we have suggested in the above discussion. In this instance, only the N-terminal residue and several residues near the C terminus[4] were identified by applying procedures to the intact peptide. Two peptides were obtained from a chymotryptic digest, and these in turn were further hydrolyzed. Only a minimum of degradation was done on each peptide until very small peptides were isolated. Amino acid composition and N- and C-terminal determinations were relied on to establish the relationship of the various pieces. Thus, the threonine in peptide Chy 2 places this portion at the N-terminal section of the original peptide, and the gluta-mic acid, valine, and lysine define the position of peptide Chy 1. From a consideration of similar information, peptides Pep 1 and Pep 2 may be related to Chy 1 and peptides Pap 1, Pap 3, and Pap 2 to Pep 1. Four enzymatic digestions were used and nine peptides were isolated in the course of this identification.

In another investigation the sequence of this same peptide was determined in a somewhat different way (Schroeder *et al.*, 1963). Seven degradations of the tryptic peptide established the partial sequence Thr-Tyr-Phe-Pro-His-Phe-Asp-(Leu, Ser$_2$, His, Gly, Ala, Glu, Val, Lys). The sequence was completed with a related chymotryptic peptide Asp-Leu-Ser-His-Gly-Ser-Ala-Gln-Val-Lys.

A Peptide from Lysozyme

Canfield (1963) has determined the amino acid sequence of a tryptic hexadecapeptide from egg white lysozyme by the means outlined in Fig. 27. The derivation of the sequence is based to a large extent on the amino acid composition of smaller peptides from the hydrolysis of the large one. When the tryptic peptide 1 was hydrolyzed with chymotrypsin, peptides 2 through 7 were isolated. The amino acid compositions of peptides 2 through 6 in conjunction with the Edman degradations of peptides 3 and 4 are sufficient to define the sequence of the C-terminal half of peptide 1. Subtilopeptidase digestion of peptide 1 yielded peptides 8 and 9 in addition to others that substanti-ated the C-terminal sequence. Peptide 10 was present in a chymo-tryptic hydrolyzate of lysozyme itself. After subtilopeptidase digestion of peptide 10, the results of the degradation of peptide 12 in conjunc-tion with the results of the degradation of peptide 1 and the amino acid compositions of peptides 8, 9, and 13 allow the sequence of peptide 1

---

[4] The arrows that point to the left in Fig. 26 denote the result of the application of carboxypeptidase.

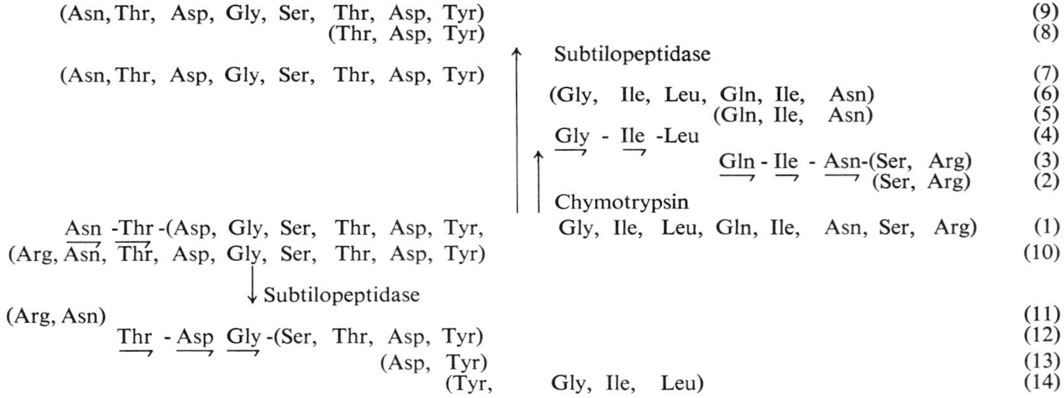

(Asn, Thr, Asp, Gly, Ser, Thr, Asp, Tyr) (9)
(Thr, Asp, Tyr) (8)

Subtilopeptidase

(Asn, Thr, Asp, Gly, Ser, Thr, Asp, Tyr) (7)

(Gly, Ile, Leu, Gln, Ile, Asn) (6)
(Gln, Ile, Asn) (5)
Gly → Ile -Leu (4)
Gln - Ile → Asn-(Ser, Arg) (3)
(Ser, Arg) (2)

Chymotrypsin
Gly, Ile, Leu, Gln, Ile, Asn, Ser, Arg) (1)

Asn →Thr-(Asp, Gly, Ser, Thr, Asp, Tyr, (1)
(Arg, Asn, Thr, Asp, Gly, Ser, Thr, Asp, Tyr) (10)

Subtilopeptidase

(Arg, Asn)
Thr → Asp Gly →(Ser, Thr, Asp, Tyr) (11)
(Asp, Tyr) (12)
(Tyr, (13)
Gly, Ile, Leu) (14)

Figure 27. Steps in the identification of a tryptic peptide from lysozyme. [Data assembled from Canfield, *J.Biol. Chem.*, **238**, 2698 (1963).]

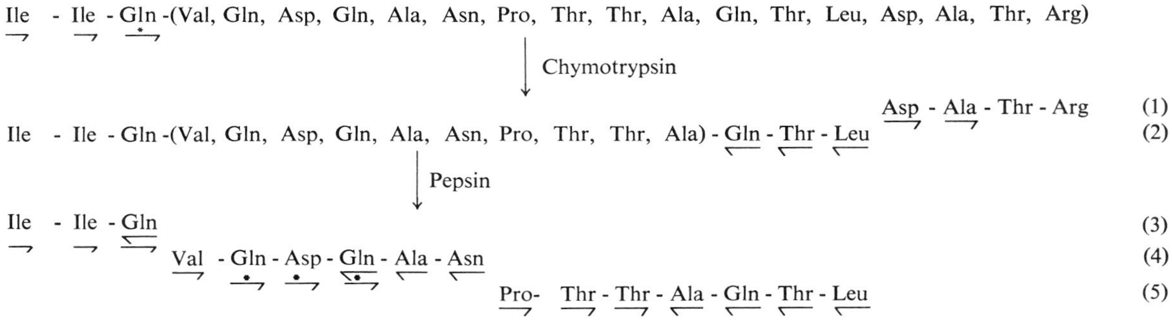

Ile → Ile → Gln -(Val, Gln, Asp, Gln, Ala, Asn, Pro, Thr, Thr, Ala, Gln, Thr, Leu, Asp, Ala, Thr, Arg)

Chymotrypsin

Ile → Ile → Gln -(Val, Gln, Asp, Gln, Ala, Asn, Pro, Thr, Thr, Ala) - Gln - Thr - Leu (1)
Asp - Ala - Thr - Arg (2)

Pepsin

Ile → Ile → Gln (3)
Val → Gln - Asp → Gln - Ala - Asn (4)
Pro- Thr → Thr - Ala - Gln - Thr - Leu (5)

Figure 28. Steps in the identification of a tryptic peptide from tobacco mosaic virus protein. [Data assembled from Anderer and Handschuh, *Z. Naturforsch.* **17b**, 536 (1962).]

to be written as given in Fig. 27 except for -(Asp, Tyr)-. The final placing of these residues in the sequence as -Asp-Tyr- is based not only on the specificity of chymotrypsin but also on peptide 14 from a peptic digest of lysozyme.

A Peptide from Tobacco Mosaic Virus Protein

Figure 28 outlines the procedure that Anderer and Handschuh (1962) applied to a tryptic peptide of tobacco mosaic virus protein. The Edman procedure identified three residues, although it did not distinguish between glutamic acid and glutamine as the asterisk is intended to signify. Chymotrypsin was used to cleave the eicosapeptide into a hexadecapeptide and a tetrapeptide. The sequence of the tetrapeptide was easily established not only by degradation but also by partial acidic hydrolysis, which yielded Ala-Thr and Thr-Arg. Peptic digestion of peptide 2 resulted in peptides 3, 4, and 5 among others. From the Edman degradation and the action of carboxypeptidase on peptide 3, the third residue of the original peptide was found to be glutamine. When these two procedures were applied to peptides 4 and 5, the indicated sequences were established except for the uncertainty in the position of the amide group in the second and third residues of peptide 4. However, when LAP was used on another peptic peptide (not shown in Fig. 28 but equivalent to peptides 4 plus 5), it was concluded that the sequence was Val-Gln-Asp-etc. It is not without interest that Fraenkel-Conrat and co-workers have deduced a different arrangement of the amide groups as we shall see in Chapter 14 (p. 182).

REFERENCES

ANDERER, F. A., AND D. HANDSCHUH (1962), Die Reihenfolge der Aminosäuren im Protein des Tabakmosaikvirus. IV. Spaltung des Tabakmosaikvirusproteins mit Trypsin, *Z. Naturforsch.*, **17b**, 536.

BARBER, M., P. JOLLES, E. VILKAS, AND E. LEDERER (1965), Determination of Amino Acid Sequences in Oligopeptides by Mass Spectrometry. I. The Structure of Fortuitine, an Acyl-nonapeptide Methyl Ester, *Biochem. Biophys. Res. Commun.*, **18**, 469.

BIEMANN, K. (1962), *Mass Spectrometry: Organic Chemical Applications*, New York, McGraw-Hill.

BRICAS, E., J. VAN HEIJENOORT, M. BARBER, W. A. WOLSTENHOLME, B. C. DAS, AND E. LEDERER (1965), Determination of Amino Acid Sequences in Oligopeptides by Mass Spectrometry. IV. Synthetic N-Acyl Oligopeptide Methyl Esters, *Biochemistry*, **4**, 2254.

CANFIELD, R. E. (1963), The Amino Acid Sequence of Egg White Lysozyme, *J. Biol. Chem.*, **238**, 2698.

EDMAN, P., AND J. SJÖQUIST (1956), Identification and Semiquantitative Determination of Phenyl Thiohydantoins, *Acta Chem. Scand.*, **10**, 1507.

FRAENKEL-CONRAT, H., J. I. HARRIS, AND A. L. LEVY (1955), Recent Developments in Techniques for Terminal and Sequence Studies in Peptides and Proteins, *Methods Biochem. Anal.*, **2**, 393.

GRAY, W. R., AND B. S. HARTLEY (1963), A Fluorescent End-Group Reagent for Proteins and Peptides, *Biochem. J.*, **89**, 59P.

KONIGSBERG, W., AND R. J. HILL (1962), The Structure of Human Hemoglobin. III. The Sequence of Amino Acids in the Tryptic Peptides of the α Chain, *J. Biol. Chem.*, **237**, 2547.

LAURSEN, R. A. (1966), A Solid-State Edman Degradation, *J. Am. Chem. Soc.*, **88**, 5344.

MC LAFFERTY, F. W. (1966), High-Resolution Mass Spectrometry, *Science*, **151**, 641.

NAUGHTON, M. A., F. SANGER, B. S. HARTLEY, AND D. C. SHAW (1960), The Amino Acid Sequence around the Reactive Serine Residue of Some Proteolytic Enzymes, *Biochem. J.*, **77**, 149.

RESSLER, C., AND D. V. KASHELIKAR (1966), Identification of Asparaginyl and Glutaminyl Residues in *endo* Position by Dehydration-Reduction, *J. Am. Chem. Soc.*, **88**, 2025.

SCHROEDER, W. A., J. R. SHELTON, J. B. SHELTON, AND J. CORMICK (1963), The Amino Acid Sequence of the α Chain of Human Fetal Hemoglobin, *Biochemistry*, **2**, 1353.

SCHROEDER, W. A., J. R. SHELTON, J. B. SHELTON, J. CORMICK, AND R. T. JONES (1963a), The Amino Acid Sequence of the γ Chain of Human Fetal Hemoglobin, *Biochemistry*, **2**, 992.

SCHROEDER, W. A., J. R. SHELTON, J. B. SHELTON, AND B. M. OLSON (1964), Some Amino Acid Sequences in Bovine-Liver Catalase, *Biochim. Biophys. Acta*, **89**, 47.

SHEMYAKIN, M. M., ET AL. (1966), Mass Spectrometric Determination of the Amino Acid Sequence of Peptides, *Nature*, **211**, 361.

SJÖQUIST, J. (1953), Paper Strip Identification of Phenyl Thiohydantoins, *Acta Chem. Scand.*, **7**, 447.

STARK, G. R. (1965), Degradation of Peptides with an Insoluble Edman Reagent, *Fed. Proc.*, **24**, 225.

12

THE OVERLAPPING OF VARIOUS TYPES OF PEPTIDES INTO THE COMPLETE SEQUENCE

If the determination of the sequence has followed the path outlined, there will have been a continual accumulating of data: the amino acid composition of the protein will be known, the N-terminal and perhaps the C-terminal residues will have been determined, tryptic peptides will have been isolated and more or less completely characterized, and chymotryptic and/or peptic peptides also will have been studied. The methods that we have been describing throughout can, in general, provide this information with relative ease and considerable speed. The amassing of this much information will provide an excellent insight into the structure of the protein. The amino acid composition will have supplied accurate data about the kind and number of each residue that must be accounted for in the final sequence. The number of isolated tryptic peptides will tell to what extent a material balance has been achieved. Is their number equal to the sum of lysyl and arginyl residues plus one (if neither a lysyl nor an arginyl residue is C-terminal)? And the chymotryptic peptides will begin to show the order in which the tryptic peptides must be arranged.

The manner in which such kinds of data are combined into the complete sequence is illustrated by Fig. 29 where the sequence of the α chain of human hemoglobins A and F is depicted. The designations T-1, T-2, etc., which point out the N-terminal residue of each tryptic peptide, are numbered in order from the N to the C terminus of the chain. Below the sequence, C-1, C-2, etc. refer to various chymotryptic peptides. The indicated chymotryptic peptides are the minimum number that are required to define this sequence.

A chromatographic separation of the tryptic peptides from the α chain is shown in Fig. 30 (modified from Schroeder et al., 1962). The number of the tryptic peptide in Fig. 29 has been used to identify each peak. This identification was possible only after the complete sequence was known, because, except in the case of T-1, the peptides do not emerge in the order in which they are present in the sequence. The use of these and other data to delineate the sequence will now be discussed on the basis of data taken largely from Hill and Konigsberg (1962).

$|$T-1 $|$ T-2   10 $|$T-3 $|$T-4
Val-Leu-Ser-Pro-Ala-Asp-Lys-Thr-Asn-Val-Lys-Ala-Ala-Trp-Gly-Lys-Val-Gly-
   $|$ $|\longleftarrow$ C-2 $\longrightarrow|\longleftarrow$ C-3 $\longrightarrow$
   $|\longleftarrow$ C-1 $\longrightarrow|$

  20   30 $|$ T-5
Ala-His-Ala-Gly-Glu-Tyr-Gly-Ala-Glu-Ala-Leu-Glu-Arg-Met-Phe-Leu-Ser-Phe-
$\longrightarrow|$ $|\longleftarrow$ C-4 $\longrightarrow|$ $|\longleftarrow$

       40 $|$ T-6
Pro-Thr-Thr-Lys-Thr-Tyr-Phe-Pro-His-Phe-Asp-Leu-Ser-His-Gly-Ser-Ala-Gln-
$\longrightarrow$C-5 $\longrightarrow|$

        $|$T-7   60 $|$T-8 $|$T-9   70
Val-Lys-Gly-His-Gly-Lys-Lys-Val-Ala-Asp-Ala-Leu-Thr-Asn-Ala-Val-Ala-His-
$|\longleftarrow$ C-6 $\longrightarrow|$
        $|\longleftarrow$ C-7 $\longrightarrow|$
                      80
Val-Asp-Asp-Met-Pro-Asn-Ala-Leu-Ser-Ala-Leu-Ser-Asp-Leu-His-Ala-His-Lys-
                                                              $|\longleftarrow$ C-8 $\longrightarrow$
                                        $|$T-12
$|$T-10 $|$T-11   100
Leu-Arg-Val-Asp-Pro-Val-Asn-Phe-Lys-Leu-Leu-Ser-His-Cys-Leu-Leu-Val-Thr-
$\longrightarrow|\longleftarrow$ C-9 $\longrightarrow|\longleftarrow$C-10$\longrightarrow|$
   110   120
Leu-Ala-Ala-His-Leu-Pro-Ala-Glu-Phe-Thr-Pro-Ala-Val-His-Ala-Ser-Leu-Asp-
                                                  $|\longleftarrow$C-11$\longrightarrow$
                                        $|$T-14
   $|$T-13   130   140
Lys-Phe-Leu-Ala-Ser-Val-Ser-Thr-Val-Leu-Thr-Ser-Lys-Tyr-Arg
$\longrightarrow|$ $|\longleftarrow$C-12$\longrightarrow|$

Figure 29. The sequence of the α chain of human hemoglobin with the tryptic and chymotryptic peptides that define the sequence.

The N-terminal sequence of the α chain was known to be Val-Leu-Ser-Pro-Ala-Asp: only T-1 fulfills this requirement and, therefore, it is placed at the N terminus. Actually, the double tryptic peptide T-1,2[1] is present in hydrolyzates, because the hydrolysis of the susceptible bond is slowed by the aspartyl residue in position 6. Consequently, no

---

[1] A designation such as T-1,2 denotes that the bond between the indicated peptides has not been cleaved.

chymotryptic peptide need be isolated to prove that T-1 and T-2 are connected. Peptide C-2 does not unequivocally link T-2 and T-3, because the sequence -Val-Lys of C-6 could equally well derive from T-2. Peptide C-1 resolves the problem and, indeed, links T-1, T-2, and T-3 together. Although a similar ambiguity obtains in the linking of T-3 and T-4 because T-7 also has the C-terminal sequence -Gly-Lys, C-7 provides the answer. Peptides C-4 through C-7 easily define the indicated ordering of peptides, but C-8 again supplies equivocal information because its leucyl residue could arise also from T-12. However, suppose that we consider data from the C terminus toward that

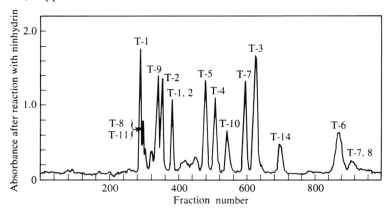

Figure 30. Chromatographic separation of the soluble tryptic peptides of the α chain of human hemoglobin. [Adapted from Schroeder *et al.*, *Anal. Chem.*, **34**, 1570 (1962). Copyright 1962 by the American Chemical Society. Reprinted by permission of the copyright owner.]

portion of sequence that has been defined. The known C-terminal sequence -Thr-Ser-Lys-Tyr-Arg in conjunction with C-12 connects T-13 and T-14. By means of C-11 and also T-12,13, peptide T-12 may be joined to T-13. Peptides T-11 and C-9 are identical in amino acid composition except for lysine and arginine, and an arginyl residue is N-terminal in C-9. This arginyl residue must derive from T-10, because the other arginyl residues are firmly placed at residues 31 and 141. Consequently, the leucyl residue of C-8 derives from T-10 and not from T-12. As a result, T-1 through T-10 and T-12 through T-14 have been put in sequence. Hence, T-11 can be placed only as indicated.

Even in this rather ideal derivation of a sequence, certain problems have had to be faced. The various types of peptides usually can be unequivocally arranged, because there is frequently a uniqueness about sequences and often about amino acid composition that shows how the several types of peptides should be matched to join them into the over-all sequence. Nevertheless, as we have seen, ambiguity can arise when identical sequences at one or the other terminus of two or more peptides require other peptides or indirect evidence to resolve the problem. However, as more and more data are obtained, longer and longer reaches of sequence that derive from various parts of the chain can be assembled. Usually one cannot combine sequences so ideally step by step from the N terminus as we have done. It is reasonable to say that this rapid accumulation of new data continues until about 75 percent of the sequence is known; then the rate of acquisition of new information decreases markedly.

This slowing of progress results in many instances from an inability to achieve a material balance. One or more tryptic peptides may be "missing"; that is, fewer tryptic peptides can be isolated than are expected from the amino acid composition of the protein. One might anticipate that, if all tryptic peptides were soluble under the conditions of a chromatographic procedure, it would be possible to detect each peptide in some part of the effluent. However, this may not be so. Some peptides seem not to be removed in discrete and detectable zones under varied (and drastic) conditions of development. A more usual situation is the presence of material (misnamed "core") that is insoluble under one or another condition at the completion of a hydrolysis.

If we return to our example of the α chain of hemoglobin, it will be seen that T-12 and T-13 are not shown in Fig. 30. Although all tryptic peptides are soluble at the pH of the digest, a precipitate forms on acidification. In their investigation, Hill and Konigsberg (1962) precipitated first with dichloracetic acid and then partially purified the redissolved precipitate by countercurrent distribution. Peptides T-12, T-13, and T-12,13 were finally purified under modified chromatographic conditions that used both Sephadex and Dowex 50.

The α chain of hemoglobin is not unique in producing such a "core." Something similar appears in the investigation of most sequences and occasions much effort before a pure peptide or peptides can be isolated. There is no generally applicable method for purifying such intractable materials. Because of such difficulties, progress toward a complete sequence may be greatly retarded.

As one avenue of approach to solving the problems, the preparation of another tryptic hydrolyzate would have to be considered. Depending upon whether any prior chemical alteration had been made, it might be desirable to oxidize, aminoethylate, or carbamidomethylate the protein. The properties of at least some of the resulting peptides might be sufficiently altered to be useful.

The investigator usually is forced to bring to bear the entire knowledge of protein chemistry and to apply any potentially useful procedure.

When the determination of sequence is in this state, when many residues have been placed in position, when much is known about the protein, and when the remaining problems are well defined, this knowledge can be used to design special experiments to obtain the missing data. For example, if no sequence is known, the result of treating a protein with cyanogen bromide may be difficult or impossible to interpret and may even be relatively worthless. Thus, if the methionyl residues were grouped rather closely together near a terminus, the protein would be largely unaltered. On the other hand, if evidence from an almost complete sequence indicated an arrangement such that cyanogen bromide treatment would provide peptides for certain overlaps, this procedure might furnish the final necessary information.

The effort and time that are required to obtain the final few percent of necessary data may be several times that to obtain all the rest. Nevertheless, the chances for complete success are good. After this goal has been reached, it may also be necessary to do more than determine merely the linear sequence of the residues. We shall now consider the means by which the position of disulfide bridges and the linkage of prosthetic groups and carbohydrate moieties may be established.

REFERENCES

HILL, R. J., AND W. KONIGSBERG (1962), The Structure of Human Hemoglobin
IV. The Chymotryptic Digestion of the α Chain of Human Hemoglobin,
J. Biol. Chem., **237**, 3151.

SCHROEDER, W. A., R. T. JONES, J. CORMICK, AND K. MC CALLA (1962), Chromatographic Separation of Peptides on Ion Exchange Resins. Separation of Peptides from Enzymatic Hydrolyzates of the α, β, and γ Chains of Human Hemoglobins, *Anal. Chem.*, **34**, 1570.

13

THE ASSIGNMENT OF THE POSITION OF DISULFIDE BRIDGES AND OF THE POINT OF THE LINKAGE OF PROSTHETIC GROUPS AND CARBOHYDRATE MOIETIES

In the foregoing chapters, we have avoided the subject of disulfide bridging and have considered the cystinyl residue in terms of its two halves and its placement in the sequence in the form of cysteic acid or some other derivative. In the history of the determination of sequence, the subject was evaded in just this way until the sequence was complete, and then only was the problem of the disulfide bridges attacked. At the present time, the identification of disulfide bridges is no longer so formidable, and some investigators have even used it as a point of departure for the determination of the sequence. If the protein contains a covalently bonded prosthetic group or is a glycoprotein, the point or points of attachment also require delineation.

THE ASSIGNMENT OF DISULFIDE BRIDGES

It is, of course, necessary to know whether there are disulfide bridges to be assigned. The presence or absence of cysteic acid in a hydrolyzate of the oxidized protein is an indicator of potential disulfide bridges. If they possibly are present, an examination of the original intact protein must be made. Basically, this is a determination by difference, because no available method is capable of a direct analytical estimate of disulfide bridges. First, the number of sulfhydryl groups must be determined. Then the difference between the number of cysteic acid residues and the number of cysteinyl residues as measured by free sulfhydryl groups will tell the number of disulfide bridges.

References for Chapter 13, pp. 168–169.

The Estimation of Free Sulfhydryl Groups

This subject with its many ramifications and problems is discussed in detail by Cecil (1963), and only the principles of pertinent methods will be outlined here.

Titration with heavy metal reagents follows the concept embodied in the following equation

$$R—S^{\ominus} + M^{\oplus} \xrightleftharpoons{\text{high pH}} R—SM.$$

The ionized sulfhydryl group represented by $RS^{\ominus}$ is allowed to react with a heavy metal $M^{\oplus}$ to yield an insoluble or at least virtually nonionized salt RSM. The common reagents are silver or mercury salts. There is some objection to titration with silver salts, because additional nonspecific binding to the protein may lead to erroneous results. If mercuric salts are used, one mercuric ion normally will react with small sulfhydryl-containing compounds as follows:

$$R—S^{\ominus} + X—Hg—X \rightarrow R—S—Hg—X + R—S^{\ominus} \rightarrow R—S—Hg—S—R.$$

Whether it does or can do the same in a protein (because of steric influences, for example) is uncertain. Consequently univalent or organomercurials such as $CH_3—Hg—X$ are commonly employed. The titration of a protein with some type of heavy metal salt is usually followed amperometrically. As long as sulfhydryl groups remain to react with the metal to form the insoluble or nonionized salt, the current will remain constant, but when the titrant is in excess, current will flow in direct proportion to the excess. By plotting current against the volume of titrant, the end point can be found, and the number of sulfhydryl groups can be calculated.

Hemoglobin provides an illustration of this procedure. When native human carbonmonoxyhemoglobin A was titrated with phenylmercuric hydroxide (Allison and Cecil, 1958), the titration curve of Fig. 31 resulted; it may be calculated from these data that 2.2 molecules of phenylmercuric hydroxide react per hemoglobin of 64,500 molecular weight and, hence, that 2.2 sulfhydryl groups are present. A determination of cysteic acid in the oxidized protein showed 5.5 cysteic acid residues or 6 for practical purposes. One is not justified, however, in concluding that there are $(6 - 2)/2$ or two disulfide bridges. If hemoglobin is denatured prior to the titration with a detergent such as sodium dodecyl sulfate, six sulfhydryl groups become available to the titrant.

These results point up the necessity of examining the protein under different conditions. The data have been confirmed in a study of the reaction with iodoacetamide in which again only two are reactive in the native protein and six in the denatured. Reaction with iodoacetamide can be used to determine sulfhydryl groups with greater certainty than by titration. In the titration, a specificity for sulfhydryl groups that may not always be true must be assumed. The reaction with iodoacetamide does not require this specificity. The fact that iodoacetamide has reacted with sulfhydryl groups follows from a positive identification of carboxymethylcysteine in a hydrolyzate, and reaction with other groups is of no consequence.

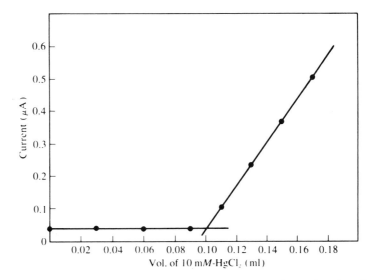

Figure 31. The titration of carbonmonoxyhemoglobin A with phenylmercuric hydroxide. [Source: Allison and Cecil, *Biochem. J.*, **69**, 27 (1958).]

Two commonly used reagents for sulfhydryl groups are *p*-chloromercuribenzoate (PCMB) and N-ethylmaleimide (NEM). Because the reaction of either compound with sulfhydryl groups produces an alteration of the spectrum, the titration can be followed spectrophotometrically. Their use has been widespread despite some problems in the interpretation of the data.

As we have already indicated, the number of disulfide bridges is deduced by difference. If this is a small difference between two large numbers, the accuracy of the result may be poor.

The Determination of the Points of Disulfide Bridging

When the locating of disulfide bridges is begun, the positions of halves of the bridges in the chain as well as the sequence in the immediate vicinity will usually be known. The general procedure follows the course of Reaction Scheme 17. The protein must first be hydrolyzed under

$$
\cdots A—B—C—\underset{\underset{\underset{\underset{\cdots P—R—M—}{|}}{S}}{|}{S}}{Cy}—D—E—F\cdots
\quad\xrightarrow{\text{Hydrolysis}}\quad
B—C—\underset{\underset{\underset{Cy}{|}}{S}}{Cy}—D
\;+\;\text{other peptides}\;\xrightarrow{(0)}
$$

... A—B—C—Cy—D—E—F ... →(Hydrolysis) B—C—Cy—D + other peptides →(0)
       | |
       S   S
       | |
       S   S
       | |
... P—R—M—Cy—Q—M—Z ...   Cy—Q—M—Z

B—C—CySO₃H—D + CySO₃H—Q—M—Z

B—C—CySO$_3$H—D + CySO$_3$H—Q—M—Z

Reaction Scheme 17.

conditions such that the disulfide bridges remain intact. After the cystine-containing peptides have been isolated, they are oxidized to the cysteic-acid-containing peptides. The isolation and characterization of the cysteic acid peptides will usually identify unambiguously the two half-cystine residues that are associated with each other.

The problem of assigning the disulfide bridges had to be faced by Sanger in the elaboration of the sequence of insulin, the first protein whose structure was completely elucidated. Ambiguous results from partial acid hydrolysis pointed up the problem of maintaining intact disulfide bonds under the conditions of hydrolysis. In a series of experiments, Ryle and Sanger (1955) showed that disulfide interchange as exemplified by

Cy   A—Cy   Cy
| | |
S   S   S
| + | ⇌ 2 |
S   S   S
| | |
Cy   A—Cy   A—Cy

was effectively prevented in 10N sulfuric acid in 30–50 percent acetic acid in the presence of thiols such as cysteine or mercaptoacetic acid, but that neutral or basic conditions should be avoided.

Although these conditions were effectively used in the case of insulin, acidic hydrolysis, as noted, has fallen from favor so that most investigators now follow the enzymatic procedures of Spackman, Stein, and Moore (1960). The most effective procedure proved to be the initial digestion of the protein with pepsin at pH 2 and subsequent cleavage with both trypsin and chymotrypsin at pH 6.5, instead of the usual higher pH, in order to maintain the integrity of the disulfide bonds. The low pH adequately denatures the protein for the attack of pepsin after which the molecule is susceptible to trypsin and chymotrypsin.

After a digest has been successfully prepared, the separation of the cystine-containing peptides may be done mainly with paper techniques as by Sanger and co-workers or with column chromatography as by Spackman, Stein, and Moore as well as others. The oxidation to cysteic acid peptides and their isolation and characterization (usually an analysis is sufficient) pose no special problems with the various methods that have been described.

A recent, so-called "diagonal" procedure of Brown and Hartley (1963) shows promise as a rapid method for identifying disulfide bridges. After a digest has been prepared, it is submitted to electrophoresis on paper at pH 6.5. The dried electropherogram is then exposed to performic acid vapor and dried again. A second electrophoresis is made at 90° to the first under the same conditions, and the peptides are detected with ninhydrin. If successive electrophoreses were carried out in this way, the spots would lie on a diagonal. The performic acid treatment, however, converts any cystine-containing peptides to cysteic-acid-containing peptides, which have a different charge and hence a different electrophoretic behavior. Those spots that are not on the diagonal are the cysteic acid peptides. The two cysteic acid peptides that fall on a line parallel to the direction of the second electrophoresis derive from a given disulfide bridge.

THE LINKAGE OF PROSTHETIC GROUPS

A prosthetic group of a protein may be defined as any group other than an amino acid or carbohydrate that is covalently or noncovalently linked to the protein. Prosthetic groups play an important role in many enzymatic reactions and are found in all degrees of weak or strong association.

If a prosthetic group is noncovalently bound, it is unlikely that chemical means will be able to determine the point of linkage. A physical method such as x-ray diffraction is the sole means at present by which it is possible to identify the nature of the interaction. Hemoglobin typifies this state of affairs. Heme which is the prosthetic group of hemoglobin and which has the structure

Hemin Chloride.

is readily removed from globin, the protein part, by mixing an aqueous solution of hemoglobin with acidified acetone. The globin precipitates and can be separated from the solution of heme. If the procedure is carefully carried out, hemoglobin can be reconstituted from the parts. The mild conditions lead to the conclusion that the linkage is noncovalent. By means of the pioneering x-ray studies of Perutz (1965), it has been shown how the heme fits into the globin moiety and with which residues it is associated. Actually, many years before the x-ray results were obtained, Wyman (discussed in detail in Wyman, 1948) interpreted titration curves of hemoglobin to mean that the imidazole side chains of two histidyl residues were involved with the iron atom of the heme group. The x-ray data verify this conclusion and also reveal various interactions of amino acid side chains with the side chains of the heme. These interactions may mainly be associated with the positioning of the heme in the protein part. The two imidazole groups play some vital but as yet undeciphered role in the functioning of the hemoglobin molecule.

Cytochrome c is the sole example of a protein in which the type of covalent linkage between protein and prosthetic group has been established. Interestingly enough, the nature of this covalent bond was deduced by Theorell (1938, 1939) long before the amino acid sequence of cytochrome c was elucidated. He hydrolyzed bovine heart cytochrome c with acid and isolated the prosthetic group (which is identical with the heme of hemoglobin) in combination with other groupings that are not present in the heme of hemoglobin. These groupings included sulfur atoms, amino groups, and carboxyl groups. Reaction with hydrobromic acid in acetic acid cleaved these atoms from the prosthetic group and released cystine. It was concluded that two cysteinyl residues were bonded at the site of the vinyl groups in the heme. Margoliash and Schejter (1966) have discussed the history of this work in detail. Years after Theorell's work, Tuppy and Paleus (1955) isolated a heme-containing peptide from a peptic hydrolyzate of beef heart cytochrome *c*. Its structure was shown to be

The two cysteinyl residues to which the heme is attached are the 14th and 17th residues in the 104-residue chain (Chapter 14, p. 174). Although chemical evidence could not determine whether the asymmetrical heme is attached as illustrated or should be rotated through 180°, the above linkage has recently been established from x-ray data (Dickerson *et al.*, 1967).

CARBOHYDRATE LINKAGES IN GLYCOPROTEINS

A glycoprotein as we have mentioned earlier (Chapter 4, p. 45) is one that contains carbohydrate. Sensitive color reactions for carbohydrates may detect their presence in protein preparations. Although this may simply be evidence of heterogeneity, there are well-documented descriptions of proteins in which a covalent link between protein and carbohydrate exists.

The study of glycoproteins has been hindered by the difficulty of performing good quantitative analyses of the carbohydrate moiety. This problem is presently in the process of solution by the use of gas chromatographic methods for volatile sugar derivatives or by means of ion-exchange chromatography of sugar-borate complexes, although the description of these procedures is beyond the province of this book. Automatic carbohydrate analyzers are in the process of development. Actually, amino sugars such as glucosamine or galactosamine may be determined with an automatic amino acid analyzer. A second important difficulty is the destruction of sugars during hydrolysis. This destruction is far more extensive usually than that of amino acids, although as noted in Chapter 5, care must be taken in the hydrolysis of glycoproteins or of proteins in the presence of carbohydrate to insure that mutual interaction does not destroy amino acids. Enzymatic methods of carbohydrate hydrolysis may be the answer to this problem.

The general approach to the study of glycoproteins has been to maintain the integrity of the carbohydrate part but to reduce the attached protein to a minimum by hydrolyzing it with nonspecific proteolytic enzymes such as those we have mentioned in Chapter 9 or by a succession of enzymes such as pepsin, trypsin, and chymotrypsin. The portion of interest is the carbohydrate with a small attached peptide. In this way, various investigators have isolated peptides with attached carbohydrate from such proteins as taka-amylase, ovalbumin, α_1-acid glycoprotein of human plasma, and several γ-globulins.

A definitive study was made by Plummer and Hirs (1964) on ribonuclease B. The investigation of this glycoprotein was much facilitated by the knowledge of the exact sequence of ribonuclease A, which had been determined through the efforts of Hirs, Moore, and Stein and which we discussed at the beginning of Chapter 1. Ribonucleases A and B occur in the pancreatic juice in the approximate ratio of 10:1 and are equally active enzymatically. Plummer and Hirs prepared a tryptic digest of reduced and cyanoethylated (Chapter 9, p. 96) ribonuclease B. The tryptic peptides were separated by means of Sephadex columns and by ion-exchange chromatography. The glycopeptide had the composition (Asp, Leu, Thr, Lys, Mannose$_6$, Glucosamine$_2$). The glucosamine may have been in the form of acetylglucosamine, although this was not determined. From ribonuclease A, a tetrapeptide of the structure Asn-Leu-Thr-Lys may be isolated. Actually, the tryptic hydrolyzate of ribonuclease B contained all the tryptic peptides that may be isolated from ribonuclease A except this tetrapeptide. After the glycotetrapeptide had been hydrolyzed by chymotrypsin, (Asp, Leu, Mannose$_6$, Glucosamine$_2$) could be isolated. From these results it was concluded that the carbohydrate was attached to the aspartyl residue by an undetermined type of bond and that the structure and sequence were

Asp-Leu-Thr-Lys
|
Mannose$_6$, Glucosamine$_2$

The carbohydrate evidently is attached at residue 34 from the N terminus in ribonuclease A. There is good evidence that residue 34 is on the surface of the molecule. The presence of this relatively large appendage does not interfere with the enzymatic activity of the molecule. Ribonucleases A and B probably are identical except for the carbohydrate in B.

The subject of glycoproteins is treated in detail in a volume edited by Gottschalk (1966).

Some components of bacterial cell walls are composed of carbohydrates and amino acids. These have been termed "mureins" and contain on the average two kinds of carbohydrate residues and four types of amino acids. This very active area of investigation has been reviewed by Martin (1966).

REFERENCES

ALLISON, A. C., AND R. CECIL (1958), The Thiol Groups of Normal Adult Human Haemoglobin, *Biochem. J.*, **69**, 27.

BROWN, J. R., AND B. S. HARTLEY (1963), The Disulphide Bridges of Chymotrypsinogen-A, *Biochem. J.*, **89**, 59P.

CECIL, R. (1963), Intramolecular Bonds in Proteins I. The Role of Sulfur in Proteins, in *The Proteins: Composition, Structure, and Function*, 2nd ed., H. Neurath, ed., New York, Academic Press, Vol. I, p. 380.

DICKERSON, R. E., M. L. KOPKA, J. WEINZERL, J. VARNUM, D. EISENBERG, AND E. MARGOLIASH (1967), Location of the Heme in Horse Heart Ferricytochrome *c* by X-ray Diffraction, *J. Biol. Chem.*, **242**, 3015.

GOTTSCHALK, A., ed. (1966), *Glycoproteins: Their Composition, Structure, and Function*, Amsterdam, Elsevier.

MARGOLIASH, E., AND A. SCHEJTER (1966), Cytochrome *c*, *Adv. Prot. Chem.*, **21**, 113.

MARTIN, H. H. (1966), Biochemistry of Bacterial Cell Walls, *Ann. Rev. Biochem.*, **35**, 457.

PERUTZ, M. (1965), Structure and Function of Haemoglobin I. A Tentative Atomic Model of Horse Oxyhaemoglobin, *J. Mol. Biol.*, **13**, 646.

PLUMMER, T. H., JR., AND C. H. W. HIRS (1964), On the Structure of Bovine Pancreatic Ribonuclease B—Isolation of a Glycopeptide, *J. Biol. Chem.*, **239**, 2530.

RYLE, A. P., AND F. SANGER (1955), Disulphide Interchange Reactions, *Biochem. J.*, **60**, 535.

SPACKMAN, D. H., W. H. STEIN, AND S. MOORE (1960), The Disulfide Bonds of Ribonuclease, *J. Biol. Chem.*, **235**, 648.

THEORELL, H. (1938), Über die chemische Konstitution des Cytochroms c, *Biochem. Z.*, **298**, 242.

THEORELL, H. (1939), *l*-Cystin aus Porphyrin c, *Enzymologia*, **6**, 88.

TUPPY, H., AND S. PALEUS (1955), Study of a Peptic Degradation Product of Cytochrome *c* I. Purification and Chemical Composition, *Acta Chem. Scand.*, **9**, 353.

WYMAN, J., JR. (1948), Heme Proteins, *Adv. Prot. Chem.*, **4**, 407.

14

THE RESULTS OF DETERMINATIONS OF SEQUENCE

Sanger's successful determination of the amino acid sequence of insulin provided, if not the first, at least more complete answers to a number of questions about proteins: they have a polypeptide structure, they have a definite arrangement of atoms as do much smaller molecules, and they may be studied by the same chemical methods by which small molecules are studied. His work, which demonstrated that it was possible to determine completely the sequence of a protein, gave impetus to other investigations that for one reason or another had the same goal. Because many investigators took up the task, the sequences of an appreciable number of proteins have been elucidated. The information in this chapter, which will list most of the published sequences, has been gained by the application of methods that have been described on the foregoing pages and by the many variations that have been employed either by choice or because of the exigencies of the work.

The data below contain representatives of each of the various classes of proteins for which a complete or virtually complete determination of sequence has been made. In some cases, the sequence to be presented will be the sole representative of the class (papain, for example), whereas in others (cytochrome *c*) many might be listed. Eck and Dayhoff (1966) have compiled an atlas of most published and some unpublished partial and complete sequences.

The order of listing below is alphabetical rather than chronological. Wherever possible, the reference is that of a detailed description of the investigation rather than of a short preliminary announcement.

References for Chapter 14, pp. 185–187.

A CATALOG OF REPRESENTATIVE SEQUENCES

Azurin (Pseudomonas fluorescens)

```
                        10                                            20
Ala-Glu-Cys-Ser-Val-Asp- Ile -Gln-Gly-Asn-Asp-Gln-Met-Gln-Phe-Asn-Thr-Asn-Ala- Ile -
                        30                                            40
Thr-Val-Asp-Lys-Ser-Cys-Lys-Gln-Phe-Thr-Val-Asn-Leu- Ser-His-Pro-Gly-Asn-Leu-Pro-
                        50                                            60
Lys-Asn-Val-Met-Gly His-Asn-Trp-Val-Leu- Ser-Thr-Ala-Ala-Asp-Met-Gln-Gly-Val-Val-
                        70                                            80
Thr-Asp-Gly-Met-Ala- Ser-Gly-Leu-Asp-Lys-Asp-Tyr-Leu-Lys-Pro-Asp-Asp-Ser-Arg-Val-
                        90                                            100
Ile -Ala-His-Thr-Lys-Leu- Ile -Gly- Ser-Gly-Glu-Lys-Asp- Ser-Val-Thr-Phe-Asp-Val-Ser-
                        110                                           120
Lys-Leu-Lys-Glu-Gly-Glu-Gln-Tyr-Met-Phe-Phe-Cys-Thr-Phe-Pro-Gly-His-Ser-Ala-Leu-

Met-Lys-Gly-Thr-Leu-Thr-Leu-Lys
```

This blue protein contains one copper atom per molecule in undetermined linkage. Among its 128 residues are three Cys/2 residues, which were identified as cysteic acid in the oxidized protein. They are not specified as cysteinyl or cystinyl residues in this investigation by Ambler and Brown (1964).

Bence–Jones Protein (Human)

```
                        10                                            20
Asp- Ile -Gln-Met-Thr-Gln-Pro- Ser- Ser- Ser-Leu- Ser-Ala- Ser-Val-Gly-Asp-Arg-Val-Thr-
                        30                                            40
Ile -Thr-Cys-Gln-Ala- Ser-Gln-(Asx¹,Ile,Asx,Ser,Phe)-Leu-Asn-Trp-Tyr-Gln-Gln-Gly-Pro-
                        50                                            60
Lys-Lys-Ala-Pro-Lys- Ile -Leu- Ile -Tyr-Asp-Ala- Ser-Asn-Leu-Glu-Thr-Gly-Val-Pro- Ser-
                        70                                            80
Arg-Phe- Ser-Gly- Ser-Gly-Phe-Gly-Thr-Asp-Phe-Thr-Phe-Thr- Ile - Ser-Gly-Leu-Gln-Pro-
                        90                                            100
Glu-Asp- Ile -Ala-Thr-Tyr-Tyr-Cys-Gln-Gln-Tyr-Asp-Thr-Leu-Pro-Arg-Thr-Phe-Gly-Gln-
                        110                                           120
Gly-Thr-Lys-Leu-Glu- Ile -Lys-Arg-Thr-Val-Ala-Ala-Pro- Ser-Val-Phe- Ile -Phe-Pro-Pro-
                        130                                           140
Ser -Asn-Glu-Gln-Leu-Lys- Ser-Gly-Thr-Ala- Ser-Val-Val-Cys-Leu-Leu-Asn-Asn-Phe-Pro-
                        150                                           160
Tyr-Arg-Glu-Ala-Lys-Val-Gln-Trp-Lys-Val-Asp-Asn-Ala-Leu-Gln- Ser-Gly-Asn- Ser-Gln-
                        170                                           180
Glu- Ser-Val-Thr-Glu-Gln-Asp- Ser-Lys-Asp- Ser-Thr-Tyr- Ser-Leu- Ser- Ser-Thr-Leu-Thr-
                        190                                           200
Leu- Ser-Lys-Ala-Asp-Tyr-Glu-Lys-His-Lys-Val-Tyr-Ala-Cys-Glu-Val-Thr-His-Gln-Gly-
                        210
Leu- Ser- Ser-Pro-Val-Thr-Lys- Ser-Phe-Asn-Arg-Gly-Glu-Cys
```

---

¹ "Asx" designates that the presence or absence of the amide group has not been determined.

The Bence–Jones proteins represent the light chains of the immunoglob-bulins. They may be isolated in quantity from individuals in certain disease states. The N-terminal half of the molecule varies with the individual, but the C-terminal appears to be invariant. This sequence was described by Titani *et. al* (1965 and 1966) and Putnam *et al.* (1966).

Chymotrypsinogen A (*Bovine*)

```
                                    10                              20
Cys-Gly-Val-Pro-Ala- Ile -Gln-Pro-Val-Leu- Ser -Gly-Leu- Ser -Arg- Ile -Val-Asn-Gly-Glu-
 I                                  30                              40
Glu-Ala-Val-Pro-Gly- Ser -Trp- Pro-Trp-Gln- Val- Ser - Leu-Gln-Asp-Lys-Thr-Gly-Phe- His-
 |                                  50                              |     60
Phe-Cys-Gly-Gly- Ser -Leu- Ile -Asn-Glu-Asn-Trp- Val- Val-Thr-Ala-Ala- His-Cys-Gly-Val-
     II                                                                 III
                                    70                              80
Thr-Thr- Ser -Asp- Val- Val- Val-Ala-Gly-Glu-Phe-Asp-Gln-Gly- Ser - Ser - Ser -Glu-Lys- Ile -
                                    90                              100
Gln-Lys-Leu-Lys- Ile -Ala-Lys- Val-Phe-Lys-Asn- Ser -Lys-Tyr-Asn- Ser -Leu-Thr- Ile -Asn-
                                    110                             120
Asn-Asn- Ile -Thr-Leu-Leu-Lys-Leu- Ser -Thr-Ala-Ala- Ser -Phe- Ser -Gln-Thr- Val- Ser -Ala-
 |                                  130                             |     140
Val -Cys-Leu-Pro- Ser - Ala- Ser -Asp-Asp-Phe-Ala-Ala-Gly-Thr-Thr-Cys- Val-Thr-Thr-Gly-
     IV                                                                 V
                                    150                             160
Trp-Gly-Leu-Thr-Arg-Tyr-Thr-Asn-Ala-Asn-Thr-Pro-Asp-Arg-Leu-Gln-Gln-Ala- Ser -Leu-
 |                                  170                             180
Pro -Leu-Leu- Ser -Asn-Thr-Asn-Cys-Lys-Lys-Tyr-Trp-Gly-Thr-Lys- Ile -Lys-Asp-Ala-Met-
                                    VI
 |                                  190        |                    200
Ile -Cys-Ala-Gly-Ala- Ser -Gly- Val- Ser - Ser -Cys-Met-Gly-Asp- Ser -Gly-Gly-Pro-Leu- Val-
     VII                                       VIII
 |                                  210                             220 |
Cys-Lys-Lys-Asn-Gly-Ala-Trp-Thr-Leu- Val-Gly- Ile -Val- Ser -Trp-Gly- Ser - Ser -Thr-Cys-
 IX                                                                     X
                                    230                             240
Ser -Thr- Ser -Thr- Pro-Gly- Val-Tyr-Ala-Arg- Val-Thr-Ala- Leu-Val-Asn-Trp- Val-Gln-Gln-

Thr-Leu-Ala- Ala-Asn
```

Disulfide bridges: I–IV; II–III; V–IX; VI–VII; and VIII–X.

The 245 residues in the single chain of chymotrypsinogen A are cross-linked by five disulfide bridges at the indicated positions. In the activa-tion of the zymogen, residues 14 and 15 (Ser-Arg) and residues 147 and 148 (Thr-Asn) are released. Chymotrypsin, therefore, has only 241 residues in three chains. Residues 1–13 (A chain) are linked to residues 16–146 (B chain) through the I–IV disulfide bridge, and the B chain is connected to residues 149–245 (C chain) through the V–IX bridge. The release of the dipeptides during activation was known long before the elucidation of the sequence of chymotrypsinogen by two indepen-dent groups. The sequence above which was reported by Brown and

Hartley (1966) after several corrections has been confirmed by the data of Meloun *et al.* (1966).

Clupeine Z (*Pacific herring*)

                  10   20
Ala -Arg-Arg-Arg-Arg- Ser -Arg-Arg-Ala- Ser -Arg-Pro- Val -Arg-Arg-Arg-Arg-Pro-Arg-Arg-
                  30
Val -Ser -Arg-Arg-Arg-Arg-Ala-Arg-Arg-Arg-Arg

Clupeine is a representative of the basic proteins called protamines, which are components of sperm. From the sequence above (Ando and Suzuki, 1966), it is apparent that two-thirds of the residues in this small protein are arginyl. No acidic amino acids are present even as the amide.

Coat Protein (*f_2 Bacteriophage*)

                  10   20
Ala - Ser -Asn-Phe-Thr-Gln-Phe- Val -Leu- Val -Asn-Asp-Gly-Gly-Thr-Gly-Asn- Val -Thr- Val -
                  30   40
Ala -Pro- Ser -Asn-Phe-Ala-Asn-Gly- Val -Ala-Glu-Trp- Ile - Ser - Ser -Asn- Ser -Arg- Ser -Gln-
                  50   60
Ala -Tyr-Lys- Val -Thr-Cys- Ser - Val -Arg-Gln- Ser - Ser -Ala-Gln-Asn-Arg-Lys-Tyr-Thr- Ile -
                  70   80
Lys- Val -Glu- Val -Pro-Lys- Val -Ala-Thr-Gln-Thr- Val -Gly-Gly- Val -Glu-Leu-Pro- Val -Ala-
                  90   100
Ala -Trp-Arg- Ser -Tyr-Leu-Asn-Leu-Glu-Leu-Thr- Ile -Pro- Ile -Phe-Ala-Thr-Asn- Ser -Asp-
                 110   120
Cys-Glu-Leu- Ile - Val -Lys-Ala Met-Gln-Gly-Leu-Leu-Lys-Asp-Gly-Asn-Pro- Ile -Pro- Ser -
Ala- Ile -Ala-Ala-Asn-Ser-Gly- Ile -Tyr

Weber and Konigsberg (1967) have reported the above sequence of the reduced and carboxymethylated derivative of this bacteriophage protein.

β-Corticotropin (*Porcine*)

                  10   20
Ser -Tyr- Ser -Met-Glu- His-Phe-Arg-Trp-Gly-Lys-Pro- Val -Gly-Lys-Lys-Arg-Arg-Pro- Val -
                  30
Lys- Val -Tyr-Pro-Asp-Gly-Ala-Glu-Asp-Gln-Leu-Ala-Glu-Ala-Phe-Pro-Leu-Glu-Phe

This hormone (also termed ACTH) was the subject of intensive investigation at about the same time that the structure of insulin was being completed. The sequence above resulted from the studies of Shepherd *et al.* (1956). Schwyzer and Sieber (1963) have described the total synthesis of the molecule; the activity equalled that of the natural product.

Cytochrome c (Human Heart)

                                        10   20
Acetyl-Gly-Asp-Val-Glu-Lys-Gly-Lys-Lys- Ile -Phe- Ile -Met-Lys-Cys- Ser -Gln-Cys-His-Thr- Val-
                                                                   └─Heme─┘
                                        30   40
Glu-Lys-Gly-Gly-Lys- His-Lys-Thr-Gly-Pro-Asn-Leu- His-Gly-Leu-Phe-Gly-Arg-Lys-Thr-
                                        50   60
Gly -Gln-Ala-Pro-Gly-Tyr- Ser -Tyr-Thr- Ala -Ala-Asn-Lys-Asn-Lys-Gly- Ile - Ile -Trp-Gly-
                                        70   80
Glu-Asp-Thr-Leu-Met-Glu-Tyr-Leu-Glu-Asn-Pro-Lys-Lys-Tyr- Ile -Pro-Gly-Thr-Lys-Met-
                                        90   100
Ile -Phe-Val-Gly- Ile -Lys-Lys-Lys-Glu-Glu-Arg-Ala-Asp-Leu- Ile -Ala-Tyr-Leu-Lys-Lys-

Ala -Thr-Asn-Glu

Cytochrome *c* has been mentioned in Chapter 13 (p. 165) as the only protein for which the covalent linkage of protein to prosthetic group has been identified. It also has an N-terminal blocking group, which in this instance is an acetyl group. The sequences of no less than 25 cytochromes *c* have been determined (Margoliash and Schejter, 1966). Many variations have been observed. Some cytochromes *c* have no N-terminal blocking group, whereas others have more or fewer residues at either N or C terminus. In a comparison of 15 cytochromes *c*, 51 residues were invariant. As might be expected, the cysteinyl residues to which the heme is attached were always present. Eleven glycyl residues were in common positions in all cases. The longest invariant sequence is one of eleven residues from positions 70 to 80. The sequence of human heart cytochrome *c* is due to Matsubara and Smith (1963).

Ferridoxin (Clostridium pasteurianum)

                                        10   20
Ala -Tyr-Lys- Ile -Ala-Asp-Ser -Cys- Val- Ser -Cys-Gly-Ala-Cys-Ala- Ser -Glu-Cys-Pro- Val-
                                        30   40
Asn-Ala- Ile - Ser -Gln-Gly Asp- Ser - Ile -Phe- Val- Ile -Asp-Ala-Asp-Thr-Cys- Ile -Asp-Cys-
                                        50
Gly -Asn-Cys-Ala-Asn- Val-Cys-Pro- Val-Gly-Ala-Pro- Val-Gln-Glu

This relatively small protein has seven sulfide and seven iron atoms associated with it. The linkage presumably is through the cysteinyl residues in some unknown way. This sequence was determined by Tanaka *et al.* (1966). The rubredoxin of *Micrococcus aerogenes*, which can replace ferredoxin in certain enzymatic reactions, also has 55 residues but only one iron atom in association with four cysteinyl residues (Backmayer *et al.*, 1967).

A plant ferrodoxin from spinach (Matsubara *et al.*, 1967) has 97 residues, which have certain similarities in sequence to the *Clostridium* ferredoxin.

Glucagon (*Bovine*)

                                         10   20
His - Ser -Gln-Gly-Thr-Phe-Thr- Ser -Asp-Tyr- Ser -Lys-Tyr-Leu-Asp- Ser -Arg-Arg-Ala-Gln-

Asp-Phe- Val -Gln-Trp-Leu-Met-Asn-Thr

Physiologically, glucagon has an action opposite to that of insulin. The structures are very different. Bromer *et al.* (1957) have elucidated the sequence.

Growth Hormone (*Human Pituitary*)

                                         10   20
Phe-Pro-Thr- Ile -Pro-Leu-Ser -Arg-Leu-Phe-Asp-Asn-Ala-Met-Leu-Arg- Ile -Leu- Ser -Leu-
                                         30   40
Glu-Leu- Ile - Ser -Trp-Leu-Glu-Pro- Val -Glu-Phe-Ala- His-Arg-Leu- His-Gln-Leu-Ala-Phe-
                                         50   60
Asp-Thr-Tyr-Glu-Glu-Phe-Glu-Glu-Ala-Tyr· Ile -Pro-Lys-Glu-Gln-Lys-Tyr- Ser -Phe-Leu-
                                         | 70   80
Gln-Asp-Pro-Glu-Thr- Ser -Leu-Cys-Phe- Ser - Ser - Ile -Glu- Ser -(Asp,Pro,Pro,Thr)-Arg-Glu-
                                         I

                                         90   100
Glu-Thr-Gln-Lys- Ser -Asp-Leu-Glu-Leu-Leu-Arg- Ser - Val -Phe-Ala-Asn- Ser -Leu- Val -Tyr-
                                         110   120
Gly- Ala- Ser -Asn- Ser -Asp- Val -Tyr-Asp-Leu-Leu-Lys-Asp-Leu-Glu-Glu-Gly- Ile -Glu-Thr-
                                         130   140
Leu-Met-Gly-Arg-Leu-Glu-Asp-Pro- Ser -Gly-Arg-Thr-Gly-Gln- Ile -Phe-Lys-Glu-Thr-Tyr-
                                         150   160
Ser -Lys-Phe-Asp-Thr-Asn- Ser - His-Asn-Asp-Asp-Ala-Leu-Leu-Lys-Asp-Tyr-Gly-Leu-Leu-
        | 170 | 180
Tyr -Cys-Phe-Arg-Lys-Asp-Met-Asp-Lys- Val -Glu-Thr-Phe-Leu-Arg- Ile - Val -Gln-Cys-Arg-
        II   III
                                         |
Ser - Val -Glu-Gly- Ser -Cys-Gly-Phe
                              IV

Disulfide bridges : I–II and III–IV.
The 188 residues of this protein have been placed in sequence by Li *et al.* (1966).

Hemoglobins (*Human*)

The following four chains in various combinations make up the several normal hemoglobins in human beings.

α CHAIN

                          10   20
Val -Leu- Ser -Pro-Ala-Asp-Lys-Thr-Asn- Val -Lys-Ala-Ala-Trp-Gly-Lys- Val -Gly-Ala- His-
                          30
Ala -Gly-Glu-Tyr-Gly-Ala-Glu-Ala-Leu-Glu-Arg-Met-Phe-Leu- Ser -Phe-Pro-Thr-Thr-Lys-
                          50   60
Thr-Tyr-Phe-Pro-His-Phe-Asp-Leu- Ser - His-Gly- Ser -Ala-Gln- Val -Lys-Gly-His-Gly-Lys-
                          70   80
Lys - Val -Ala-Asp-Ala-Leu-Thr-Asn-Ala- Val -Ala-His- Val -Asp-Asp-Met-Pro-Asn-Ala Leu-
                          90   100
Ser -Ala-Leu- Ser -Asp-Leu- His-Ala- His-Lys-Leu-Arg- Val -Asp-Pro- Val -Asn-Phe-Lys-Leu-
                          110   120
Leu- Ser - His-Cys-Leu-Leu- Val -Thr-Leu-Ala-Ala- His-Leu-Pro-Ala-Glu-Phe-Thr-Pro-Ala-
                          130   140
Val - His-Ala- Ser -Leu-Asp-Lys-Phe-Leu-Ala- Ser - Val- Ser -Thr- Val -Leu-Thr- Ser -Lys-Tyr-
Arg

Detailed data may be found in Hill and Konigsberg (1962).

β CHAIN

                          10   20
Val - His- Leu-Thr- Pro-Glu-Glu-Lys- Ser -Ala-Val-Thr-Ala-Leu-Trp-Gly-Lys- Val-Asn- Val-
                          30   40
Asp-Glu- Val -Gly-Gly-Glu- Ala-Leu-Gly-Arg-Leu-Leu- Val - Val -Tyr-Pro-Trp-Thr-Gln-Arg-
                          50   60
Phe-Phe-Glu- Ser -Phe-Gly-Asp-Leu- Ser -Thr-Pro-Asp-Ala- Val-Met-Gly-Asn-Pro-Lys- Val-
                          70   80
Lys - Ala- His-Gly-Lys-Lys- Val -Leu-Gly-Ala-Phe- Ser -Asp-Gly-Leu-Ala- His-Leu-Asp-Asn-
                          90   100
Leu-Lys-Gly-Thr-Phe-Ala-Thr-Leu- Ser -Glu-Leu- His-Cys-Asp-Lys-Leu- His- Val -Asp-Pro-
                          110   120
Glu-Asn-Phe-Arg-Leu-Leu-Gly-Asn- Val -Leu- Val -Cys- Val -Leu-Ala- His- His-Phe-Gly-Lys-
                          130   140
Glu-Phe-Thr-Pro-Pro- Val -Gln-Ala-Ala- Tyr-Gln-Lys- Val- Val -Ala-Gly- Val -Ala-Asn-Ala-
Leu-Ala- His-Lys-Tyr- His

Braunitzer *et al.* (1961) may be consulted for more information about
this sequence.

γ CHAIN

                          10   20
Gly-His-Phe-Thr-Glu-Glu-Asp-Lys-Ala-Thr- Ile -Thr- Ser -Leu-Trp-Gly-Lys- Val-Asn- Val-
                          30   40
Glu-Asp-Ala-Gly-Gly-Glu-Thr-Leu-Gly-Arg-Leu-Leu- Val- Val -Tyr-Pro-Trp-Thr-Gln-Arg-
                          50   60
Phe-Phe-Asp- Ser -Phe-Gly-Asn-Leu- Ser - Ser -Ala- Ser -Ala- Ile -Met-Gly-Asn-Pro-Lys- Val-
                          70   80
Lys -Ala- His-Gly-Lys-Lys- Val -Leu-Thr- Ser -Leu-Gly-Asp-Ala- Ile -Lys-His-Leu-Asp-Asp-
                          90   100
Leu-Lys-Gly-Thr-Phe-Ala-Gln-Leu- Ser -Glu-Leu- His-Cys-Asp-Lys-Leu- His- Val -Asp-Pro-
                          110   120
Glu-Asn-Phe-Lys-Leu-Leu-Gly-Asn- Val-Leu- Val -Thr- Val -Leu-Ala- Ile - His-Phe-Gly-Lys-
                          130   140
Glu-Phe-Thr-Pro-Glu- Val -Gln-Ala- Ser -Trp-Gln-Lys-Met- Val -Thr-Gly- Val -Ala- Ser -Ala-
Leu- Ser - Ser -Arg-Tyr- His

This sequence has been described by Schroeder *et al.* (1963).

δ CHAIN

```
                    10                                        20
Val -His-Leu-Thr-Pro-Glu-Glu-Lys-Thr-Ala- Val-Asn-Ala-Leu-Trp-Gly-Lys-Val-Asn-Val-
                    30                                        40
Asp-Ala- Val-Gly-Gly-Glu-Ala-Leu-Gly-Arg-Leu-Leu- Val- Val-Tyr-Pro-Trp-Thr-Gln-Arg-
                    50                                        60
Phe-Phe-Glu- Ser -Phe-Gly-Asp-Leu- Ser - Ser -Pro-Asp-Ala- Val-Met-Gly-Asn-Pro-Lys-Val-
                    70                                        80
Lys -Ala- His-Gly-Lys-Lys- Val-Leu-Gly-Ala-Phe- Ser -Asp-Gly-Leu-Ala- His-Leu-Asp-Asn-
                    90                                        100
Leu-Lys-Gly-Thr-Phe- Ser -Gln-Leu- Ser -Glu-Leu- His-Cys-Asp-Lys-Leu- His- Val-Asp-Pro-
                    110                                       120
Glu-Asn-Phe-Arg-Leu-Leu-Gly-Asn- Val-Leu- Val-Cys- Val-Leu-Ala-Arg-Asn-Phe-Gly-Lys-
                    130                                       140
Glu-Phe-Thr-Pro Gln-Met-Gln-Ala-Ala-Tyr-Gln-Lys- Val- Val-Ala-Gly- Val-Ala-Asn-Ala-

Leu-Ala- His-Lys-Tyr- His
```

The sequence of the δ chain was determined through the efforts of several groups [see Schroeder and Jones (1965) for references].

In the normal adult human, hemoglobin A, which is the major component, is composed of two α and two β chains and may be given the subunit formula $\alpha_2\beta_2$. Each chain has one heme group (p. 165) associated with it in noncovalent linkage. The developing fetus and young infant (less than three months of age) has hemoglobin F or $\alpha_2\gamma_2$ (again with a heme group for each chain) as the main homoglobin component. A minor component termed hemoglobin A_2 is present in the normal adult to the extent of 2 to 3 percent and has the subunit structure $\alpha_2\delta_2$. Although another hemoglobin, $\alpha_2\varepsilon_2$, is believed to be present very early in fetal life, little is known about the ε chains. It will be observed that a pair of α chains is common to each of these hemoglobins. None has a disulfide bridge.

Other minor components are also being investigated. A minor fetal component differs from F in the presence of an N-terminal acetyl group on one γ chain, whereas one in the adult has an unidentified N-terminal blocking group on a β chain (see also p. 79).

Many so-called abnormal human hemoglobins have been detected. Most are variants of hemoglobin A, although a few of F and of A_2 are also known. In almost all instances, the difference between the variant and normal hemoglobins lies in the substitution at a single position of one type of amino acid residue for another. Thus, in hemoglobin S, a valyl and not a glutamyl residue occupies the sixth position of the two β chains: this constitutes the entire difference between the two types. The investigation of abnormal human hemoglobins has been actively pursued. As a result, when this book went to press, the nature of the aberration in more than 50 abnormal hemoglobins had been elucidated.

Complete or almost complete sequences for several animal hemoglobins are known. Reviews by Huehns and Shooter (1965) and Schroeder and Jones (1965) provide references to other reviews and to research papers on many phases of hemoglobin and its properties.

The three-dimensional structure of horse hemoglobin has been determined by means of x-ray diffraction through the efforts of Perutz and collaborators (Perutz, 1965).

Insulin (Bovine)

```
                          ┌─────────10─────────┐                                    20
Gly- Ile -Val-Glu-Gln-Cys-Cys-Ala- Ser- Val-Cys- Ser -Leu-Tyr-Gln-Leu-Glu-Asn-Tyr-Cys-Asn
                          │                  10                                      ╱20
Phe- Val-Asn-Gln- His-Leu-Cys-Gly- Ser- His-Leu- Val-Glu-Ala-Leu-Tyr-Leu- Val-Cys-Gly-Glu-
                                          30
Arg-Gly-Phe-Phe-Tyr-Thr-Pro-Lys-Ala
```

As has been mentioned several times in this book, Sanger and collaborators (Ryle *et al.*, 1955) achieved the first complete determination of the sequence of a protein in the case of insulin. Simple as this protein is in comparison to many whose sequences are given in this chapter, it is worthy of note that Sanger had to solve almost all problems that must still be solved in sequence determinations. For example, he had to separate two types of chain after breaking disulfide bridges, to isolate peptides after various cleavages of the polypeptide chain, to identify the position of amide groups, and to establish the positions of the previously broken disulfide bridges. In this, he established methods of approaching these problems that are still in use today.

The total synthesis of insulin has also been achieved (Katsoyannis, 1966).

Lysozyme (Chicken Egg White)

```
         │              10                                    20
Lys- Val- Phe-Gly-Arg-Cys-Glu-Leu-Ala-Ala-Ala-Met-Lys-Arg- His-Gly-Leu-Asp-Asn-Tyr-
         I
                       30│                                    40
Arg-Gly-Tyr- Ser -Leu-Gly-Asn-Trp- Val -Cys-Ala-Ala-Lys-Phe-Glu- Ser -Asn-Phe-Asn-Thr-
                        II
                       50                                     60
Gln-Ala-Thr-Asn-Arg-Asn-Thr-Asp-Gly- Ser -Thr-Asp-Tyr-Gly- Ile -Leu-Gln- Ile -Asn- Ser-
         │              70                              │            80 │
Arg-Trp-Trp-Cys-Asn-Asp-Gly-Arg-Thr-Pro-Gly- Ser -Arg-Asn-Leu-Cys-Asn- Ile -Pro-Cys
         III                                          IV            V
                       90                              │            100
Ser -Ala-Leu-Leu- Ser- Ser -Asp- Ile -Thr-Ala- Ser- Val-Asn-Cys-Ala-Lys-Lys- Ile -Val- Ser-
                                          VI
```

110 | 120
Asp-Gly-Asp-Gly-Met-Asn-Ala-Trp-Val-Ala-Trp-Arg-Asn-Arg-Cys-Lys-Gly-Thr-Asp-Val-
                                                            VII
              |
Gln-Ala-Trp- Ile -Arg-Gly-Cys-Arg-Leu
                    VIII

Disulfide bridges: I–VIII; II–VII; III–V; and IV–VI.
Lysozyme is a protein that hydrolyzes carbohydrates of cell walls and
so disrupts bacterial membranes. The above sequence derives from the
efforts of Jolles and collaborators (Jolles *et al.*, 1965) and of Canfield
and colleagues (Canfield and Liu, 1965). The sequence is that of Canfield and differs from the data of Jolles who reports Gln-Ala-Thr at
residues 40–42, aspartic acid at 46, asparagine at 48, Asn-Ile at 58 and
59, and Asn-Val at 92 and 93. The three-dimensional structure of
lysozyme is known from x-ray investigations (Blake *et al.*, 1965).

Lysozyme (*T4 Bacteriophage*)

                    10   20
Met-Asn- Ile -Phe-Glu-Met-Leu-Arg- Ile -Asp-Glu-Gly-Leu-Arg-Leu-Lys- Ile -Tyr-Lys-Asp-
                    30   40
Thr-Glu-Gly-Tyr-Tyr-Thr- Ile -Gly- Ile -Gly-His-Leu-Leu-Thr-Lys- Ser -Pro- Ser -Leu-Asn-
                    50   60
Ala -Ala-Lys- Ser -Gln-Leu-Asp-Lys-Ala- Ile -Gly-Arg-Asn- Cys-Asn-Gly-Val- Ile -Thr-Lys-
                    70   80
Asp-Glu-Ala-Glu-Lys-Leu-Phe-Asn-Gln-Asp- Val-Asp-Ala-Ala-Val-Arg-Gly- Ile -Leu-Arg-
                    90   100
Asn-Ala-Lys-Leu-Lys-Pro-Val-Tyr-Asp- Ser -Leu-Asp-Ala-Val-Arg-Arg-Cys-Ala-Leu- Ile -
                    110   120
Asn-Met-Val-Phe-Gln-Met-Gly-Glu-Thr-Gly- Val-Ala-Gly-Phe-Thr-Asn- Ser -Leu-Arg-Met-
                    130   140
Leu-Gln-Gln-Lys-Arg-Trp-Asp-Glu-Ala-Ala- Val-Asn-Leu-Lys-Tyr-Asn-Gln-Thr-Pro-Asn-
                    150   160
Arg-Ala-Lys-Arg-Val- Ile -Thr-Thr-Phe-Arg-Thr-Gly-Thr-Trp-Asp-Ala-Tyr-Lys-Asn-Leu

This protein, which is produced in the host cells of *Escherichia coli*
after infection with bacteriophage, has properties similar to that of
other lysozymes (above). However, the structures of this lysozyme
(Inouye and Tsugita, 1966) and of egg white lysozyme are distinctly
different. The lengths of the chains are dissimilar, and the sequences
show little resemblance to each other. In contrast to egg white lysozyme
with its four disulfide bridges, this bacteriophage lysozyme has none.

Myoglobin (*Sperm Whale*)

                    10   20
Val -Leu- Ser -Glu-Gly-Glu-Trp-Gln-Leu-Val-Leu-His-Val-Trp-Ala-Lys-Val-Glu-Ala-Asp-
                    30   40
Val -Ala-Gly-His-Gly-Gln-Asp- Ile -Leu- Ile -Arg-Leu-Phe-Lys- Ser -His-Pro-Glu-Thr-Leu-

```
                              50                                    60
Glu-Lys-Phe-Asp-Arg-Phe-Lys-His-Leu-Lys-Thr-Glu-Ala-Glu-Met-Lys-Ala-Ser-Glu-Asp-
                              70                                    80
Leu-Lys-Lys-His-Gly-Val-Thr-Val-Leu-Thr-Ala-Leu-Gly-Ala- Ile -Leu-Lys-Lys-Lys-Gly-
                              90                                    100
His -His-Glu-Ala-Glu-Leu-Lys-Pro-Leu-Ala-Gln-Ser-His-Ala-Thr-Lys-His-Lys- Ile -Pro-
                              110                                   120
Ile -Lys-Tyr-Leu-Glu-Phe- Ile -Ser-Glu-Ala- Ile - Ile -His-Val-Leu-His-Ser-Arg-His-Pro-
                              130                                   140
Gly-Asn-Phe-Gly-Ala-Asp-Ala-Gln-Gly-Ala-Met-Asn-Lys-Ala-Leu-Glu-Leu-Phe-Arg-Lys-
                              150
Asp- Ile -Ala-Ala-Lys-Tyr-Lys-Glu-Leu-Gly-Tyr-Gln-Gly
```

Whereas hemoglobin is the carrier of oxygen, myoglobin stores oxygen in the tissues. Like hemoglobin, it also has a noncovalently attached heme group. The molecule of myoglobin consists of a single chain instead of four as does hemoglobin. There are certain similarities in the sequence of myoglobin and of the individual chains of hemoglobin. The three-dimensional structures of myoglobin and of individual hemoglobin chains are almost identical. The determination of this sequence is due to Edmundson (1965). The three-dimensional structure resulted from the work of Kendrew and co-workers (Kendrew, 1962).

Papain (Papaya Latex)

```
                              10                                    20
Ile -Pro-Glu-Tyr-Val-Asp-Trp-Arg-Gln-Lys-Gly-Ala-Val-Thr-Pro-Val-Lys-Asn-Gln-Gly-
 |                            30                                    40
Ser -Cys-Gly-Ser-Cys-Trp- (Ala-Phe)(Ile-Ile) -Arg-Asn-Thr-Pro-Tyr-Tyr-Glu-Gly-Val-Gln-
 I             II
 |                            50                                    60
Arg-Tyr-Cys-Arg-Ser-Arg-Glu-Lys-Gly-Pro-Tyr-Ala-Ala-Lys-Thr-Asp-Gly-Val-Arg-Gln-
 III
                              70                                    80
Val -Gln-Pro-Tyr-Asn-Gln-Gly-Ala-Leu-Leu-Tyr-Ser- Ile -Ala-Asn-Gln-Pro-Ser-Val-Val-
                              90                                    100 |
Leu-Gln-Ala-Ala-Gly-Lys-Asp-Phe-Gln-Leu-Tyr-Arg-Gly-Gly- Ile -Phe-Val-Gly-Pro-Cys-
                                                                      IV
                              110                                   120
Gly-Asn-Lys-Val-Asp-His-Ala-Val-Ala-Ala-Val-Gly-Tyr-Asn-Pro-Gly-Tyr- Ile -Leu- Ile -
                              130                                   140
Lys-Asn-Ser-Trp-Gly-Thr-Gly-Trp-Gly-Glu-Asn-Gly-Tyr- Ile -Arg- Ile -Lys-Thr-Gly-Asn-
                              150            |                           | 160
Leu-Asn-Gln-Tyr-Ser-Glu-Gln-Glu-Leu-Leu-Asp-Cys-Asp-Arg-Arg-Ser-Tyr-Gly-Cys-Tyr-
                                             V                            VI
                              170                                   180
Pro-Gly-Asp-Gly-Trp-(Ser-Ala-Leu)-Val-Ala-Gln-Tyr-Gly- Ile -His-Tyr-Arg-Gly-Thr-Gly-
                  |           190
Asn-Ser-Tyr-Gly-Val-Cys-Gly-Leu-Tyr-Thr-Ser-Ser-Phe-Tyr-Pro-Val-Lys-Asn
                  VII
```

Disulfide bridges: III–V; IV–VII; and I–VI; II is sulfhydryl.

Papain contains four disulfide bridges and, in addition, a sulfhydryl group that must be free if the protein is to be active as a proteolytic enzyme. A few features of the structure of this protein remain to be completed because not all overlapping peptides have been isolated despite the extensive efforts of Smith and co-workers (Light *et al.*, 1964).

Ribonuclease A (Bovine)

The sequence of ribonuclease has already been presented in Fig. 1 on p. 2. Some of its properties that were discussed in Chapter 1 will be enlarged upon in concluding Chapter 15. The sequence of ribonuclease was determined in the laboratories of Moore and Stein mainly through the efforts of Hirs.

Ribonuclease B (Bovine)

It will be recalled (Chapter 13, p. 167) that ribonuclease B is believed to differ from ribonuclease A only in the attachment of a carbohydrate moiety at residue 34.

Ribonuclease T₁ (Aspergillus oryzae)

```
          |                    |            10 |                                              20
Ala -Cys-Asp-Tyr-Thr-Cys-Gly- Ser -Asn-Cys-Tyr- Ser - Ser - Ser -Asp- Val- Ser -Thr-Ala-Gln-
 I                   II             III
                                    30                                                          40
Ala - Ala-Gly-Tyr-Gln-Leu- His-Glu-Asp-Gly-Glu-Thr- Val-Gly- Ser -Asn- Ser -Tyr-Pro- His-
                              50                                                          60
Lys- Tyr-Asn-Asn-Tyr-Glu-Gly-Phe-Asp-Phe- Ser - Val- Ser - Ser -Pro-Tyr-Tyr-Glu-Trp-Pro-
                              70                                                          80
Ile  -Leu- Ser - Ser -Gly-Asp- Val-Tyr- Ser -Gly- Pro-Gly- Ser -Gly-Ala-Asp-Arg- Val- Val-Phe-
                              90                                                         100
Asn-Glu-Asn-Asn-Gln-Leu-Ala-Gly- Val- Ile -Thr- His-Thr-Gly-Ala- Ser -Gly-Asn-Asn-Phe-
          |
Val -Glu-Cys-Thr
          IV
```

Disulfide bridges: I–III and II–IV.
Ribonuclease T₁ has a different specificity toward ribonucleic acid than does ribonuclease A. Its distinctly different sequence has been reported by Takahashi (1965).

Subtilisin (Carlsberg) (Bacillus subtilis)

```
                    10                                              20
Ala -Gln-Thr- Val-Pro-Tyr-Gly- Ile -Pro-Leu- Ile - Lys-Ala-Asp-Lys- Val-Gln-Ala-Gln-Gly-
                    30                                              40
Phe-Lys-Gly-Ala-Asn- Val-Lys- Val-Ala- Val-Leu-Asp-Thr-Gly- Ile -Gln-Ala- Ser - His-Pro-
                    50                                              60
Asn-Leu-Asn- Val- Val-Gly-Gly-Ala- Ser -Phe- Val-Ala-Gly-Gln-Ala-Tyr-Asn-Thr-Asp-Gly-
```

70   80

Asn-Gly-His-Gly-Thr-His-Val-Ala-Gly-Thr-Val-Ala-Ala-Leu-Asn-Asn-Thr-Thr-Gly-Val-

90   100

Leu-Gly-Val-Ala-Pro-Ser-Val-Ser-Leu-Tyr-Ala-Val-Lys-Val-Leu-Asn-Ser-Ser-Gly-Ser-

110   120

Gly-Ser-Tyr-Ser-Gly-Ile-Val-Ser-Gly-Ile-Gln-Trp-Ala-Thr-Thr-Asn-Gly-Met-Asp-Val-

130   140

Ile-Asn-Met-Ser-Leu-Gly-Gly-Ala-Ser-Gly-Ser-Thr-Ala-Met-Lys-Gln-Ala-Val-Asp-Asn-

150   160

Ala-Tyr-Ala-Arg-Gly-Val-Val-Val-Val-Ala-Ala-Ala-Gly-Asn-Ser-Gly-Asn-Ser-Gly-Ser-

170   180

Thr-Asn-Thr-Ile-Gly-Tyr-Pro-Ala-Lys-Tyr-Asp-Ser-Val-Ile-Ala-Val-Gly-Ala-Val-Asp-

190   200

Ser-Asn-Ser-Asn-Arg-Ala-Ser-Phe-Ser-Ser-Val-Gly-Ala-Glu-Leu-Glu-Val-Met-Ala-Pro-

210   220

Gly-Ala-Gly-Val-Tyr-Ser-Thr-Tyr-Pro-Thr-Asn-Thr-Tyr-Ala-Thr-Leu-Asn-Gly-Thr-Ser-

230   240

Met-Ala-Ser-Pro-His-Val-Ala-Gly-Ala-Ala-Ala-Leu-Ile-Leu-Ser-Lys-His-Pro-Asn-Leu-

250   260

Ser-Ala-Ser-Gln-Val-Arg-Asn-Arg-Leu-Ser-Ser-Thr-Ala-Thr-Tyr-Leu-Gly-Ser-Ser-Phe-

270

Tyr-Tyr-Gly-Lys-Gly-Leu-Ile-Asn-Val-Gln-Ala-Ala-Ala-Gln

This bacterial proteinase like trypsin and chymotrypsin has been used in sequence determinations (see p. 106). Unlike these enzymes, it does not require activation of a zymogen. Although there are similarities in the action of the three enzymes and although trypsin and chymotrypsin have many common features of structure, subtilisin shows no similarity in structure to the other two enzymes (Smith et al., 1966).

Tobacco Mosaic Virus Protein

10   20

Acetyl-Ser-Tyr-Ser-Ile-Thr-Thr-Pro-Ser-Gln-Phe-Val-Phe-Leu-Ser-Ser-Ala-Trp-Ala-Asp-Pro-

30   40

Ile-Glu-Leu-Ile-Asn-Leu-Cys-Thr-Asn-Ala-Leu-Gly-Asn-Gln-Phe-Gln-Thr-Gln-Gln-Ala-

50   60

Arg-Thr-Val-Gln-Val-Arg-Gln-Phe-Ser-Gln-Val-Trp-Lys-Pro-Ser-Pro-Gln-Val-Thr-Val-

70   80

Arg-Phe-Pro-Asp-Ser-Asp-Phe-Lys-Val-Tyr-Arg-Tyr-Asn-Ala-Val-Leu-Asp-Pro-Leu-Val-

90   100

Thr-Ala-Leu-Leu-Gly-Ala-Phe-Asp-Thr-Arg-Asn-Arg-Ile-Ile-Glu-Val-Glu-Asn-Gln-Ala-

110   120

Asn-Pro-Thr-Thr-Ala-Glu-Thr-Leu-Asp-Ala-Thr-Arg-Arg-Val-Asp-Asp-Ala-Thr-Val-Ala-

130   140

Ile-Arg-Ser-Ala-Ile-Asn-Asn-Leu-Ile-Val-Glu-Leu-Ile-Arg-Gly-Thr-Gly-Ser-Tyr-Asn-

150

Arg-Ser-Ser-Phe-Glu-Ser-Ser-Ser-Gly-Leu-Val-Trp-Thr-Ser-Gly-Pro-Ala-Thr

Although the protein whose sequence is given here is relatively small, about 3000 of these subunits (p. 85) are associated with nucleic acid to form the virus. The sequences of the proteins from several natural strains of the virus have been studied as well as those of artificially produced mutants. The above data about the "common" virus protein are due to the efforts of Fraenkel-Conrat and co-workers (Funatsu and Fraenkel-Conrat, 1964) and of Anderer and Handschuh (1962). Anderer reports results slightly at variance with the above sequence of Fraenkel-Conrat: glutamine at residues 95, 97, and 106, aspartic acid at 98, and Asp-Ile at 125 and 126 (see also Fig. 28, p. 152).

Trypsin Inhibitor (Bovine Pancreas)

<pre>
            | 10 | 20
Arg-Pro-Asp-Phe-Cys-Leu-Glu-Pro-Pro-Tyr-Thr-Gly-Pro-Cys-Lys-Ala-Arg- Ile -Arg-Tyr-
                I   II
                          | 30 | 40
Phe-Tyr-Asn-Ala-Lys-Ala-Gly-Leu-Cys-Gln-Thr-Phe-Val-Tyr-Gly-Gly-Cys-Arg- Ala-Lys-
                              III   IV
                          50 | |
Arg-Asn-Asn-Phe-Lys- Ser -Ala-Glu-Asp-Cys-Met-Arg-Thr-Cys-Gly-Gly-Ala
                               V   VI
</pre>

Disulfide bridges: I–VI; II–IV; and III–V.
The structure of this small, highly crosslinked protein has been described by three groups (Chauvet *et al.*, 1964; Kassell *et al.*, 1965; Dlouha *et al.*, 1966). The above sequence is taken from Dlouha *et al.* However, the three reports differ appreciably among themselves.

Trypsinogen (Bovine)

<pre>
                          10 | 20
Val -Asp-Asp-Asp-Asp-Lys- Ile -Val-Gly-Gly-Tyr-Thr-Cys-Gly-Ala-Asn-Thr-Val-Pro-Tyr-
                                           I
                          30 | 40
Gln-Val- Ser -Leu-Asn- Ser -Gly-Tyr-His-Phe-Cys-Gly-Gly- Ser -Leu- Ile -Asn- Ser -Gln-Trp-
                              II
               | 50   60
Val -Val- Ser -Ala-Ala-His-Cys-Tyr-Lys- Ser -Gly- Ile -Gln-Val-Arg-Leu-Gly-Glu-Asp-Asn-
               III
                          70   80
Ile -Asn-Val-Val-Glu-Gly-Asp-Glu-Gln-Phe- Ile - Ser -Ala- Ser -Lys- Ser - Ile -Val-His-Pro-
                          90   100
Ser -Tyr-Asn-(Pro,Leu,Thr,Asn)-Asn-Asn-Asp- Ile -Met-Leu- Ile -Lys-Leu-Lys- Ser -Ala-Ala-
                         110 | 120
Ser -Leu-Asn- Ser -Arg-Val-Ala- Ser - Ile - Ser -Leu-Pro-Thr- Ser -Cys-Ala- Ser -Ala-Gly-Thr-
                                                   IV
  | 130   140
Gln-Cys-Leu- Ile - Ser -Gly-Trp-Gly-Asn-Thr-Lys- Ser - Ser -Gly-Thr- Ser -Tyr-Pro-Asp-Val-
  V
  | 150 | 160
Leu-Lys-Cys-Leu-Lys-Ala-Pro- Ile -Leu- Ser -Asp- Ser - Ser -Cys-Lys- Ser -Ala-Tyr-Pro-Gly-
  VI   VII
                         | 170 | 180
Gln- Ile -Thr- Ser -Asn-Met-Phe-Cys-Ala-Gly-Tyr-Leu-Glu-Gly-Gly-Lys-Asn- Ser -Cys-Gln-
                              VIII   IX
</pre>

```
                                    | 190                              200
Gly-Asp-Ser-Gly-Gly-Pro-Val-Val-Cys-Ser-Gly-Lys-Leu-Gln-Gly- Ile -Val-Ser-Trp-Gly-
                                    X
      |                             210                |              220
Ser -Gly-Cys-Ala-Gln-Lys-Asn-Lys-Pro-Gly-Val-Tyr-Thr-Lys-Val-Cys-Asn-Tyr-Val-Ser-
      XI                                               XII
Trp- Ile -Lys-Gln-Thr- Ile -Ala-Ser-Asn
```

Disulfide bridges: I–VI; II–III; IV–XII; V–X; VII–VIII; and IX–XI.

When trypsinogen is activated to form trypsin, residues 1–6 are removed. In this respect, it differs markedly from chymotrypsinogen (p. 172). Although trypsin and chymotrypsin have dissimilar specificity, their precursors arise in the same organ and have many similarities in sequence (Walsh and Neurath, 1964). These authors as well as a group of Czech investigators (Mikes *et al.*, 1967) are responsible for the determination of the sequence. Mikes *et al.* report the presence of amide groups on residues 58, 67, 68, and 151 and the sequence Ser-Asn-Thr-Leu at residues 84–87.

Tryptophan Synthetase A (α Subunit)

```
                      10                                   20
Met-Gln-Arg-Tyr-Glu-Ser-Leu-Phe-Ala-Gln-Leu-Lys-Glu-Arg-Lys-Glu-Gly-Ala-Phe-Val-
                      30                                   40
Pro-Phe-Val-Thr-Leu-Gly-Asp-Pro-Gly- Ile -Glu-Gln-Ser-Leu-Lys- Ile -Asp-Thr-Leu-Ile-
                      50                                   60
Glu-Ala-Gly-Ala-Asp-Ala-Leu-Glu-Leu-Gly- Ile -Pro-Phe-Ser-Asp-Pro-Leu-Ala-Asp-Gly-
                      70                                   80
Pro-Thr- Ile -Gln-Asn-Ala-Thr-Leu-Arg-Ala-Phe-Ala-Ala-Gly-Val-Thr-Pro-Ala-Gln-Cys-
                      90                                   100
Phe-Glu-Met-Leu-Ala-Leu- Ile -Arg-Gln-Lys-His-Pro-Thr- Ile -Pro- Ile -Gly-Leu-Leu-Met-
                      110                                  120
Tyr-Ala-Asn-Leu-Val-Phe-Asn-Lys-Gly- Ile -Asp-Glu-Phe-Tyr-Ala-Gln-Cys-Glu-Lys-Val-
                      130                                  140
Gly-Val-Asp-Ser-Val-Leu-Val-Ala-Asp-Val-Pro-Val-Gln-Glu-Ser-Ala-Pro-Phe-Arg-Gln-
                      150                                  160
Ala-Ala-Leu-Arg-His-Asn-Val-Ala-Pro- Ile -Phe- Ile -Cys-Pro-Pro-Asn-Ala-Asp-Asp-Asp-
                      170                                  180
Leu-Leu-Arg-Gln- Ile -Ala-Ser-Tyr-Gly-Arg-Gly-Tyr-Thr-Tyr-Leu-Leu-Ser-Arg-Ala-Gly-
                      190                                  200
Val-Thr-Gly-Ala-Glu-Asn-Arg-Ala-Ala-Leu-Pro-Leu-Asn-His-Leu-Val-Ala-Lys-Leu-Lys-
                      210                                  220
Glu-Tyr-Asn-Ala-Ala-Pro-Pro-Leu-Gln-Gly-Phe-Gly- Ile -Ser-Ala-Pro-Asp-Gln-Val-Lys-
                      230                                  240
Ala-Ala- Ile -Asp-Ala-Gly-Ala-Ala-Gly-Ala- Ile -Ser-Gly-Ser-Ala- Ile -Val-Lys- Ile - Ile -
                      250                                  260
Glu-Gln-His-Asn- Ile -Glu-Pro-Glu-Lys-Met-Leu-Ala-Ala-Leu-Lys-Val-Phe-Val-Gln-Pro-

Met-Lys-Ala-Ala-Thr-Arg-Ser
```

Yanofsky *et al.* (1967) who determined the sequence of this protein have used these data and those of mutants to study the colinear relationship between the genetic map of a gene and this protein that is its product.

COMMENTS

When Hirs, Moore, and Stein first presented a sequence of ribonuclease, they described it as a "working hypothesis" of the structure of the molecule. As subsequent events proved, their cautious attitude was warranted and some revisions were necessary. Somewhat the same attitude must temper one's consideration of the data in this chapter. When two or more groups have reported the sequence of the same protein, there is usually slight disagreement. This can only mean that the determination of sequence is sometimes a less exact science than one would like. Nevertheless, the results are impressive.

Exact references to the data in this chapter have been given. Slightly different versions may sometimes be found in other publications of some authors as they correct "typographical errors" or alter already published sequences without explanation.

REFERENCES

AMBLER, R. P., AND L. H. BROWN (1964), The Amino Acid Sequence of *Pseudomonas fluorescens* Azurin, *J. Mol. Biol.*, **9**, 825.

ANDERER, F. A., AND D. HANDSCHUH (1962), Die Reihenfolge der Aminosäuren im Protein des Tabakmosaikvirus. IV. Spaltung des Tabakmosaikvirusproteins mit Trypsin, *Z. Naturforsch.*, **17b**, 536.

ANDO, T., AND K. SUZUKI (1966), The Amino Acid Sequence of the Second Component of Clupeine, *Biochim. Biophys. Acta*, **121**, 427.

BACKMAYER, H., K. T. YASUNOBU, AND H. R. WHITELEY (1967), The Amino Acid Sequence of *Micrococcus aerogenes* Rubredoxin, *Biochem. Biophys. Res. Commun.*, **26**, 435.

BLAKE, C. C. F., D. F. KOENIG, G. A. MAIR, A. C. T. NORTH, D. C. PHILLIPS, AND V. R. SARMA (1965), Structure of Hen Egg-White Lysozyme—A Three-Dimensional Fourier Synthesis at 2 Å Resolution, *Nature*, **206**, 757.

BRAUNITZER, G., R. GEHRING-MÜLLER, N. HILSCHMANN, K. HILSE, G. HOBOM, V. RUDLOFF, AND B. WITTMANN-LIEBOLD (1961), Die Konstitution des normalen adulten Humanhämoglobins, *Z. physiol. Chem.*, **325**, 283.

BROMER, W. W., L. G. SINN, AND O. K. BEHRENS (1957), The Amino Acid Sequence of Glucagon. V. Location of Amide Groups, Acid Degradation Studies and Summary of Sequential Evidence, *J. Am. Chem. Soc.*, **79**, 2807.

BROWN, J. R., AND B. S. HARTLEY (1966), Location of Disulphide Bridges by Diagonal Paper Electrophoresis. The Disulphide Bridges of Bovine Chymotrypsinogen A, *Biochem. J.*, **101**, 214.

CANFIELD, R. E., AND A. K. LIU (1965), The Disulfide Bonds of Egg White Lysozyme (Muramidase), *J. Biol. Chem.*, **240**, 1997.

CHAUVET, J., G. NOUVEL, AND R. ACHER (1964), Structure Primaire d'un Inhibiteur Pancreatique de la Trypsine (Inhibiteur de Kunitz et Northrop), *Biochim. Biophys. Acta*, **92**, 200.

DLOUHA, V., D. POPISILOVA, B. MELOUN, AND F. SORM (1966), On Proteins. C. Disulfide Bonds of Basic Trypsin Inhibitor from Beef Pancreas, *Collection Czech. Chem. Commun.*, **31**, 346.

ECK, R. V., AND M. O. DAYHOFF (1966), *Atlas of Protein Sequence and Structure 1966*, Silver Spring, Maryland, The National Biomedical Research Foundation.

EDMUNDSON, A. B. (1965), Amino-Acid Sequence of Sperm Whale Myoglobin, *Nature*, **205**, 883.

FUNATSU, G., AND H. FRAENKEL-CONRAT (1964), Location of Amino Acid Exchanges in Chemically Evoked Mutants of Tobacco Mosaic Virus, *Biochemistry*, **3**, 1357.

HILL, R. J., AND W. KONIGSBERG (1962), The Structure of Human Hemoglobin. IV. The Chymotryptic Digestion of the α Chain of Human Hemoglobin, *J. Biol. Chem.*, **237**, 3151.

HUEHNS, E. R., AND E. M. SHOOTER (1965), Haemoglobin, *Science Progr.*, **52**, 353.

INOUYE, M., AND A. TSUGITA (1966), The Amino Acid Sequence of T4 Bacteriophage Lysozyme, *J. Mol. Biol.*, **22**, 193.

JOLLES, P., D. CHARLEMAGNE, J.-F. PETIT, A.-C. MAIRE, AND J. JOLLES (1965), Biochimie Comparee des Lysozymes, *Bull. Soc. Chim. Biol.*, **47**, 2241.

KASSELL, B., M. RADICEVIC, M. J. ANSFIELD, AND M. LASKOWSKI, SR. (1965), The Basic Trypsin Inhibitor of Bovine Pancreas. IV. The Linear Sequence of the 58 Amino Acids, *Biochem. Biophys. Res. Commun.*, **18**, 255.

KATSOYANNIS, P. G. (1966), Synthesis of Insulin, *Science*, **154**, 1509.

KENDREW, J. C. (1962), Side-Chain Interactions in Myoglobin, in *Enzyme Models and Enzyme Structure*, a Symposium held June 4–6, 1962, Brookhaven National Laboratory, Upton, N.Y.

LI, C. H., W.-K. LIU, AND J. S. DIXON (1966), Human Pituitary Growth Hormone. XII. The Amino Acid Sequence of the Hormone, *J. Am. Chem. Soc.*, **88**, 2050.

LIGHT, A., R. FRATER, J. R. KIMMEL, AND E. L. SMITH (1964), Current Status of the Structure of Papain: The Linear Sequence, Active Sulfhydryl Group, and the Disulfide Bridges, *Proc. Nat. Acad. Sci. U.S.*, **52**, 1276.

MARGOLIASH, E., AND A. SCHEJTER (1966), Cytochrome *c*, *Adv. Prot. Chem.*, **21**, 113.

MATSUBARA, H., R. M. SASAKI, AND R. K. CHAIN (1967), The Amino Acid Sequence of Spinach Ferredoxin, *Proc. Nat. Acad. Sci. U.S.*, **57**, 439.

MATSUBARA, H., AND E. L. SMITH (1963), Human Heart Cytochrome *c*. Chymotryptic Peptides, Tryptic Peptides, and the Complete Amino Acid Sequence, *J. Biol. Chem.*, **238**, 2732.

MELOUN, B., I. KLUH, V. KOSTKA, L. MORAVEK, Z. PRASIK, J. VANECEK, B. KEIL, AND F. SORM (1966), Covalent Structure of Bovine Chymotrypsinogen A, *Biochim. Biophys. Acta*, **130**, 543.

MIKES, O., V. TOMASEK, V. HOLEYSOVSKY, AND F. SORM (1967), On Proteins. CVI. Covalent Structure of Bovine Trypsinogen, *Collection Czech. Chem. Commun.*, **32**, 655.

PERUTZ, M. F. (1965), Structure and Function of Hemoglobin I. A Tentative Atomic Model of Horse Oxyhaemoglobin, *J. Mol. Biol.*, **13**, 646.

PUTNAM, F. W., K. TITANI, AND E. WHITLEY, JR. (1966), Chemical Structure of Light Chains: Amino Acid Sequence of Type K Bence-Jones Proteins, *Proc. Roy. Soc. London*, **166B**, 124.

RYLE, A. P., F. SANGER, L. F. SMITH, AND R. KITAI (1955), The Disulphide Bonds of Insulin, *Biochem. J.*, **60**, 541.

SCHROEDER, W. A., AND R. T. JONES (1965), Some Aspects of the Chemistry and Function of Human and Animal Hemoglobins, *Fortschr. Chem. Org. Naturstoffe*, **23**, 113.

SCHROEDER, W. A., J. R. SHELTON, J. B. SHELTON, J. CORMICK, AND R. T. JONES (1963), The Amino Acid Sequence of the γ Chain of Human Fetal Hemoglobin, *Biochemistry*, **2**, 992.

SCHWYZER, R., AND P. SIEBER (1963), Total Synthesis of Adrenocorticotropic Hormone, *Nature*, **199**, 172.

SHEPHERD, R. G., S. D. WILLSON, K. S. HOWARD, P. H. BELL, D. S. DAVIES, S. B. DAVIS, E. A. EIGNER, AND N. E. SHAKESPEARE (1956), Studies with Corticotropin. III. Determination of the Structure of β-Corticotropin and its Active Degradation Products, *J. Am. Chem. Soc.*, **78**, 5067.

SMITH, E. L., F. S. MARKLAND, C. B. KASPER, R. J. DE LANGE, M. LANDON, AND W. H. EVANS (1966), The Complete Amino Acid Sequence of Two Types of Subtilisin, BPN' and Carlsberg, *J. Biol. Chem.*, **241**, 5974.

TAKAHASHI, K. (1965), The Amino Acid Sequence of Ribonuclease T_1, *J. Biol. Chem.*, **240**, PC4117.

TANAKA, M., T. NAKASHIMA, A. BENSON, H. MOWER, AND K. T. YASUNOBU (1966), The Amino Acid Sequence of *Clostridium pasteurianum* Ferredoxin, *Biochemistry*, **5**, 1666.

TITANI, K., E. WHITLEY, JR., L. AVOGARDO, AND F. W. PUTNAM (1965), Immunoglobulin Structure: Partial Amino Acid Sequence of a Bence Jones Protein, *Science*, **149**, 1090.

TITANI, K., E. WHITLEY, JR., AND F. W. PUTNAM (1966), Immunoglobulin Structure: Variation in the Sequence of Bence Jones Proteins, *Science*, **152**, 1513.

WALSH, K. A., AND H. NEURATH (1964), Trypsinogen and Chymotrypsinogen as Homologous Proteins, *Proc. Nat. Acad. Sci. U.S.*, **52**, 884.

WEBER, K., AND W. KONIGSBERG (1967), Amino Acid Sequence of the f_2 Coat Protein, *J. Biol. Chem.*, **242**, 3563.

YANOFSKY, C., G. R. DRAPEAU, J. R. GUEST, AND B. C. CARLTON (1967), The Complete Amino Acid Sequence of the Tryptophan Synthetase A Protein (α Subunit) and its Colinear Relationship with the Genetic Map of a Gene, *Proc. Nat. Acad. Sci. U.S.*, **57**, 296.

15

THE PROSPECT BEFORE US

The object of discussing the prospect before us is not to attempt to prophesy what the most useful procedures for sequence determination will be in a few years. It would have been a rash prophet who in 1956 would have predicted such an advance in methodology that today one would be able to write all of the sequences in the preceding chapter. It may of course happen, as some have ventured, that high resolution mass spectrometry will be the method of choice for sequence determination in a few years. Possibly, the automatic "Edman machine" will come into vogue (Edman and Begg, 1967; see also pp. 75 and 90). Perhaps the future will lie in the application of clever and well-thought-out chemical procedures.

THE EXAMPLE OF RIBONUCLEASE

In considering the prospect before us, we would take up again the theme of Chapter 1 and ask of what value is the knowledge of a sequence after the effort to elucidate it has been made. In doing this, the opportunity arises to consider ingenious approaches to the solution of various problems. Ribonuclease, which served as an example in Chapter 1, will again be the basis for these comments. The sequence of ribonuclease as it is depicted in Fig. 1 (p. 2) and as it is reproduced again in Fig. 32 gives no idea of the three-dimensional arrangement of the polypeptide chain, although this drawing is made to show the disulfide bonds. However, we want now to consider what may be learned about the three-dimensional structure of a protein by chemical studies if the sequence is established. In doing this, we make the premise that the various reactive groups in a protein will be influenced in their reactivity

188   References for Chapter 15, pp. 198–199.

by their environment in much the same way as they are in a small molecule. For example, a double bond and an aldehyde group will have altered properties if they are conjugated rather than isolated. So

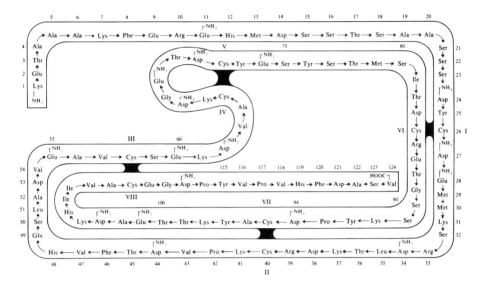

Figure 32.   The amino acid sequence of ribonuclease. [Source: Smyth, Stein, and Moore, *J. Biol. Chem.*, **238**, 227 (1963).]

we assume that this occurs also in a protein molecule, where various amino, carboxyl, imidazole, phenolic, and other reactive groups are present.

Reaction with Iodoacetic Acid

Let us consider in more detail the information that was briefly discussed at the beginning of Chapter 1. Pertinent references may be found in the paper of Crestfield, Moore, and Stein (1963).

At alkaline pH, iodoacetic acid carboxymethylates the ε-amino groups of lysyl residues in ribonuclease, and at low pH the sulfur of methionyl residues reacts. However, at pH 5.5 only one of four histidyl residues is altered in the native protein and none in the oxidized, reduced, or denatured protein. Iodoacetamide, a neutral molecule, does not react.

When the reaction mixture of native ribonuclease and iodoacetic acid at pH 5.5 was chromatographed, two products in addition to unaltered ribonuclease were isolated. The major reaction product was 119-(1-CM-His)-RNase[1] which has the structure

whereas the minor product, which always occurred in 1:8 ratio with the major product, was 12-(3-CM-His)-RNase or

Although the major product is completely inactive, the other has a few percent of activity. The two are alternate products, whose ratio is independent of the time of reaction or the ratio of iodoacetic acid to ribonuclease over a wide range. Other halogenated acids react in rather different ratios; some may attack one or the other histidyl residue exclusively (Heinrikson *et al.*, 1965).

From these and other data, the general spatial arrangement of imidazole side chains and iodoacetic acid at the time of reaction is suggested to be somewhat as follows:

Low pK   Normal or higher pK

---

[1] RNase is a common abbreviation for ribonuclease.

The iodoacetic acid is held near the reacting imidazole nitrogen by a positive charge. This is deduced because of the nonreactivity of iodo-acetamide. The reaction occurs preferentially at an unprotonated nitrogen. Consequently a close positive charge, which would lower the pK of the imidazole group and which may be present on the second imidazole group, is inferred. Whether or not this be the actual mecha-nism, it is apparent that these histidyl residues have unique positions, that spatially they must be very close though separated by many residues in the sequence, and that they are vital for the functioning of the enzyme.

Reaction with Dinitrofluorobenzene

Although complete dinitrophenylation is ordinarily desired in the study of N-terminal residues, Hirs and Kycia (1965) have obtained meaningful results from the slow and incomplete reaction of DNFB with ribonuclease. At pH 8 where ribonuclease is active, the acetate form of the protein was allowed to react at 15°C until 20 percent inacti-vation had occurred. The main product was identified as 41-ε-DNP-RNase, that is, the DNP-group was attached to the ε-amino group of the lysyl residue in position 41. Other products were 1-α-DNP-RNase; 7,41-bis-ε-DNP-RNase; and 1-α,41-ε-bis-DNP-RNase. Only 1-α-DNP-RNase had activity (60 percent of that of ribonuclease).

These rather complex results were interpreted on the basis of a study of the reaction rates of amino groups in simple peptides. In the latter, the α-amino group reacts approximately ten times as rapidly as the ε-amino group. The 1-α-amino group of ribonuclease was dinitro-pheylated at about the same rate as that in peptides, but the 41-ε-amino group was dinitrophenylated at a rate approximately ten times that of the 1-α-amino group. Accordingly, the 41-ε-amino group had a reaction rate approximately 70 times that of the ε-amino group in Gly-Lys. The unusual reactivity of the 41-ε-amino group is attributed to the proximity of a positively charged group. The effect of competitive inhibitors of ribonuclease on the reactivity of the 41-ε-amino group is interpreted to mean that it is an essential part of the active site. When the active site is disrupted by the dinitrophenylation of the 41-ε-amino group, the 7-ε-amino group is unmasked and becomes reactive. The rate of reaction of the 7-ε-amino group is about that of the α-amino group of small peptides and therefore appreciably higher than that of the normal ε-amino group. The 7-ε-amino group is assumed to have a role in the active site of the molecule.

Further evidence of the proximity and interplay of the 41- and 7-ε-amino groups was obtained through the reaction of the crosslinking agent 1,5-difluoro-2,4-dinitrobenzene (Marfey *et al.*, 1965). Under conditions that minimize intermolecular reaction, the major product had a crosslink between the 41- and 7-ε-amino groups.

Taken together, the data suggest that the imidazole groups of residues 12 and 119 and the ε-amino groups of residues 7 and 41 are important components of the active site. Other experiments of rather different nature which give added support to these conclusions will be described later.

Crosslinking with a Diimido Ester

Hartman and Wold (1966) have applied the bifunctional reagent dimethyl adipimidate

$$Cl^{\ominus}H_2\overset{\oplus}{N}=C—(CH_2)_4—C=\overset{\oplus}{N}H_2Cl^{\ominus}$$
$$\underset{OCH_3 \quad CH_3O}{|\qquad\qquad\qquad\quad|}$$

to ribonuclease. The reaction with amino groups is the same as that of methyl acetimidate (Chapter 9, p. 103). If two amino groups have the correct spatial relationship, the bifunctional reagent should crosslink parts of the molecule just as 1,5-difluoro-2,4-dinitrobenzene does. Hartman and Wold concluded that crosslinks had been made between the amino groups of lysyl residues at positions 1 and 7, 7 and 37, and 31 and 37.

Reaction with N-Carboxy-D,L-Alanine Anhydride

When N-carboxy-D,L-alanine anhydride is allowed to react with a protein (Cooke *et al.*, 1963), the following conversion takes place

$$
\begin{array}{c}
\text{HN—CO}\\
\text{Protein—NH}_2 + \quad | \quad \rangle\!O \rightarrow \text{Protein—NH—CO—CH—NH}_2 + CO_2\\
\text{CH}_3\text{—C—CO} \qquad\qquad\qquad\qquad |\\
\text{H} \qquad\qquad\qquad\qquad\qquad\quad \text{CH}_3
\end{array}
$$

Because the reaction itself introduces a new amino group, continued reaction will yield a product that has polyalanyl chains on each α- or ε-amino group. When this reagent was applied to ribonuclease, all the anticipated groups reacted with the exception of the ε-amino groups of lysyl residues at 7, 37, and 41. It was concluded that other lysyl groups are exposed on the surface of the molecule. This special behavior on the part of groups at residues 7 and 41 is not unexpected in view of their situation. Apparently, residue 37 also is in different surroundings than the others, although it is not obvious whether the active site or some other feature is involved.

Reaction of Carboxyl Groups

The so-called "spectrophotometric titration"[2] of ribonuclease is interpreted to mean that three tyrosyl residues are "normal" and three are "abnormal" in the ionizing properties of their hydroxyl group. Other evidence suggests that the three abnormal residues are associated with carboxyl groups. Because these carboxyl groups presumably should have abnormal properties, the experiments now to be described were devised (Riehm *et al.*, 1965).

In these studies ribonuclease was esterified with methanolic hydrogen chloride. These are admittedly abnormal conditions, and it may reasonably be questioned whether the protein is in its native state during the reaction. However, the enzymatically inactive product had properties that suggested at least a reasonably close relation to the native state; thus, at least two tyrosyl residues were still abnormal by spectrophotometric titration.

Ribonuclease contains eleven potential points of esterification— five glutamyl, five aspartyl, and the C-terminal valyl residues. The Lossen rearrangement was the basis for examining the product in order to determine which groups had been esterified. The details of this rearrangement are given in Reaction Scheme 18. Hence, an esterified aspartyl residue appears in a complete hydrolyzate as 2,3-diamino-

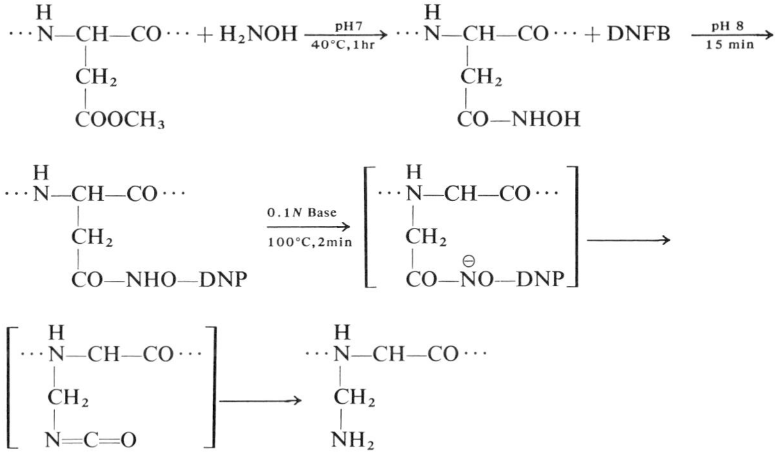

Reaction Scheme 18.

[2] When tyrosine is taken to a high pH, the phenolic hydroxyl group ionizes. The spectrum of the ionized form is different from that of the nonionized form at low pH. When the spectrum of a protein is examined as a function of pH, the quantitative changes can be correlated with the number of phenolic hydroxyl groups that are or are not ionizing normally. This is termed a spectrophotometric titration.

propionic acid and an esterified glutamyl residue as 2,4-diaminobutyric acid, and both may be determined with an amino acid analyzer.

In this way it was learned that three aspartyl residues did not esterify. These three were identified as the aspartyl residues at positions 14, 38, and 83 and, accordingly, are considered to be in association with tyrosyl residues.

Reaction with Iodine

To identify the abnormal tyrosyl residues, reaction with iodine has been used (Woody et al., 1966). Under proper conditions, iodination of tyrosyl residues occurs. In the reaction product, spectrophotometric titration shows the presence of three noniodinated and still abnormal tyrosyl residues. The conclusion was reached that the abnormal tyrosyl residues were those in positions 25, 92, and 97.[3]

On the basis of evidence which will not be described, it has been concluded that these tyrosyl residues pair with aspartyl residues in the following way: Tyr 25-Asp 14, Tyr 92-Asp 38, and Tyr 97-Asp 83 (Li et al., 1966). Different pairings were suggested in earlier work.

Tyrosine is nitrated by tetranitromethane under mild conditions (Sokolovsky et al., 1966). If this reaction is applied to ribonuclease, it will be interesting to see whether the results agree with those of iodination.

Limited Enzymatic Hydrolysis

Subtilisin (or subtilopeptidase) has been mentioned in Chapter 9 as a rather unspecific proteolytic enzyme. Under certain conditions, however, its action on ribonuclease may be limited to the cleavage of a single peptide bond (Richards and Vithayathil, 1959). The reaction product, termed ribonuclease S, is fully active and may be separated chromatographically from native ribonuclease. Ribonuclease S in turn may be resolved into S-protein and S-peptide by precipitation with trichloracetic acid or by passage through a column of Sephadex. S-Peptide is composed of residues 1 to 20 (or 21) from the N terminus of ribonuclease, and the remainder is S-protein. Although neither S-protein nor S-peptide alone is active, they may be combined to a product with full activity.

To determine which of the residues in S-peptide are essential to

---

[3] It must not be supposed that this conclusion was reached in as simple a way as this brief description would imply.

activity, Hofmann and collaborators (1966) have synthesized S-peptide as well as many related peptides and have determined to what extent activity is regained when they are combined with the natural S-protein. Table 10 presents qualitatively their quantitative data from a few of the

TABLE 10.   *Activity of Combinations of Synthetic Peptides with Native S-Protein*

Residue nos. in peptide[a]	Activity	Conclusion
1–20	Full	Synthetic S-peptide identical with native
1–13	Excellent	Residue 12 necessary for activity; residue 13 improves activity
1–12	Fair	
1–11	None	
2–13	Good	N-Terminal lysyl residue unnecessary
3–13	None	Glutamyl residue in position 2 necessary

[a] These numbers correspond to residues in order from the N terminus of ribonuclease.

combinations and points out the conclusions that may be drawn. We see again the necessity of residue 12. Residue 2 is important, but residue 1 is not. The function of some residues, perhaps residue 2 among them, may be to hold S-peptide and S-protein in the correct spatial relationship. In the intact protein, these residues presumably maintain the proper configuration of the N-terminal part of the molecule to the remainder.

Hybridization

When ribonuclease is lyophilized from a 50 percent aqueous solution of acetic acid, aggregates of higher molecular weight are formed. The dimer, which is the aggregate in largest amount, has a specific activity equal to that of the monomer. Disaggregation occurs if a solution of pH 6.5 is maintained at 65°C for 15 min.

If the ribonuclease molecule in Fig. 32 is drawn schematically in this way

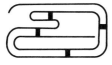

the first step toward dimerization is assumed to be an unfolding of the N-terminal portion thus

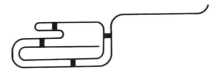

Dimerization takes place when two unfolded molecules combine so

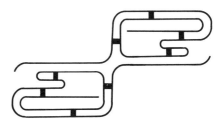

As already discussed, when iodoacetic acid reacts with ribonuclease, the inactive 119-(1-CM-His)-RNase and the slightly active 12-(3-CM-His)-RNase are formed. If an equal mixture of these derivatives were unfolded and dimerized, one of the products should have the essential features for activity as this equation shows.

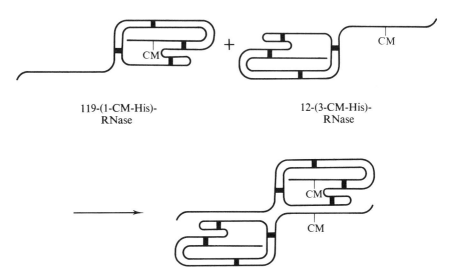

That an active product can be isolated from such a reaction mixture is further evidence of how vital residues 12 and 119 are. Moore, Stein, and collaborators have been responsible for these experiments (Fruchter and Crestfield, 1965).

Miscellaneous

Diazomethane is a reagent that may be used for esterification. Riehm and Scheraga (1965) have investigated the reaction of diazo-acetoglycinamide with ribonuclease. The product of reaction with a carboxyl group in the protein would be

Protein—COOH + N_2—CH_2—CO—NH—CH_2—CO—NH_2 →

$\qquad$ Protein—COO—CH_2—CO—NH—CH_2—CO—NH_2 + N_2

Hydolysis will yield the normal amino acids of the protein, HO-CH_2-COOH, glycine, and ammonia; that is, the extent of any reaction can be determined by the increased glycine content of the hydrolyzate. Because ribonuclease contains only three glycyl residues, the reaction of even one group may be detected easily. Although a maximum of three carboxyl groups reacted under certain conditions, that of the aspartyl residue in position 53 was especially reactive. The product was fully active enzymatically.

It should be mentioned that, if the N-terminal residue of ribonuclease is removed, the molecule is active, but if four residues at the C terminus are taken away, the activity is lost.

If the disulfide bridges of ribonuclease are reduced and the molecule is denatured, enzymatic activity is lost. However, by careful oxidation the correct disulfide bridges are again formed, and activity is regained (Epstein *et al.*, 1962). These data are interpreted to mean that the sequence itself contains the necessary information to determine the three-dimensional or tertiary structure. Friedman *et al.* (1966) have studied the reduction of several iodinated derivatives and the regain of their activity. They conclude that tyrosyl residue 115 in its protonated form contains a necessary piece of information for the process of resuming the native configuration.

Conclusions

These chemical reactions that have been successfully applied to ribonuclease permit some definite conclusions to be drawn about the active site of the molecule, about differences in the relative reactivity of identical groups toward specific reagents, and about the proximity of certain residues to each other. The information is all the more welcome because ribonuclease has not fully yielded its three-dimensional structure to x-ray investigation.

On the basis of the chemical evidence, Hammes and Scheraga (1966) have proposed a three-dimensional model of ribonuclease, which was devised to satisfy the chemical data that have been presented above. Preliminary reports of two x-ray investigations have also been published. Kartha, Bello, and Harker (1967) have described a model on the basis of a resolution of 2 Å, whereas Avey *et al.* (1967) have achieved a resolution of 5.5 Å. The structures derived from x-ray diffraction are very different from that deduced from the chemical data. Unfortunately, the two structures by x-ray diffraction do not agree. The data of Kartha, Bello, and Harker has been presented in sufficient detail that one can compare them with the chemical data. As would be expected, the histidyl residues at positions 12 and 119 are spatially near to each other and to the lysyl residue at position 41. The lysyl residue at position 7 also could interact. The pairing of tyrosyl and aspartyl residues at positions 25 and 14 as well as 92 and 38 apparently can occur, but that of 97 and 83 is unlikely. The first 20 residues from the N terminus are somewhat apart from the remainder of the molecule; S-peptide apparently could be cleaved without much disturbance of the remainder of the molecule. At the present state of knowledge, it is not obvious what forces hold S-peptide and S-protein so exactly that this modified enzyme has full activity. After the x-ray data are further refined, it will be interesting to see the exact nature of interactions that have or have not been detected by the chemical studies.

REFERENCES

AVEY, H. P., M. O. BOLES, C. H. CARLISLE, S. A. EVANS, S. J. MORRIS, R. A. PALMER, B. A. WOOLHOUSE, AND S. SHALL (1967), Structure of Ribonuclease *Nature*, **213**, 557.

COOKE, J. P., C. B. ANFINSEN, AND M. SELA (1963), The Identification of Unreactive Amino Groups in Ribonuclease and Their Significance to Enzymatic Activity, *J. Biol. Chem.*, **238**, 2034.

CRESTFIELD, A. M., W. H. STEIN, AND S. MOORE (1963), Properties and Conformation of the Histidine Residues at the Active Site of Ribonuclease, *J. Biol. Chem.*, **238**, 2421.

EDMAN, P., AND G. BEGG (1967), A Protein Sequenator, *European J. Biochem.*, **1**, 80.

EPSTEIN, C. J., R. F. GOLDBERGER, D. M. YOUNG, AND C. B. ANFINSEN (1962), A Study of the Factors Influencing the Rate and Extent of Enzymic Reactivation during Reoxidation of Reduced Ribonuclease, *Arch. Biochem. Biophys.*, *Suppl.* **1**, 223.

FRIEDMAN, M. E., H. A. SCHERAGA, AND R. F. GOLDBERGER (1966), Structural Studies of Ribonuclease. XXVI. The Role of Tyrosine 115 in the Refolding of Ribonuclease, *Biochemistry*, **5**, 3770.

FRUCHTER, R. G., AND A. M. CRESTFIELD (1965), On the Structure of Ribonuclease Dimer. Isolation and Identification of Monomers Derived from
Inactive Carboxymethyl Dimers, *J. Biol. Chem.*, **240**, 3875.

HAMMES, G. G., AND H. A. SCHERAGA (1966), A Model of Ribonuclease Based
on Chemical Evidence, *Biochemistry*, **5**, 3690.

HARTMAN, F. C., AND F. WOLD (1966), Bifunctional Reagents. Crosslinking
of Pancreatic Ribonuclease with a Diimido Ester, *J. Am. Chem. Soc.*,
88, 3890.

HEINRIKSON, R. L., W. H. STEIN, A. M. CRESTFIELD, AND S. MOORE (1965), The
Reactivities of the Histidine Residues at the Active Site of Ribonuclease
toward Halo Acids of Different Structures, *J. Biol. Chem.*, **240**, 2921.

HIRS, C. H. W., AND J. H. KYCIA (1965), Identification of Initial Reaction Sites
in the Dinitrophenylation of Bovine Pancreatic Ribonuclease A, *Arch.
Biochem. Biophys.*, **111**, 223.

HOFMANN, K., M. J. SMITHIRS, AND F. M. FINN (1966), Studies on Polypeptides.
XXXV. Synthesis of S-Peptide $_{1-20}$ and its Ability to Activate S-Protein,
J. Am. Chem. Soc., **88**, 4107.

KARTHA, G., J. BELLO, AND D. HARKER (1967), Tertiary Structure of Ribonuclease, *Nature*, **213**, 862.

LI, L.-K., J. P. RIEHM, AND H. A. SCHERAGA (1966), Structural Studies of Ribonuclease. XXIII. Pairing of the Tyrosyl and Carboxyl Groups, *Biochemistry*, **5**, 2043.

MARFEY, P. S., M. UZIEL, AND J. LITTLE (1965), Reaction of Bovine Pancreatic
Ribonuclease A with 1,5-Difluoro-2,4-dinitrobenzene. II. Structure of an
Intramolecularly Bridged Derivative, *J. Biol. Chem.*, **240**, 3270.

RICHARDS, F. M., AND P. J. VITHAYATHIL (1959), The Preparation of Subtilisin-
modified Ribonuclease and the Separation of the Peptide and Protein
Components, *J. Biol. Chem.*, **234**, 1459.

RIEHM, J. P., C. A. BROOMFIELD, AND H. A. SCHERAGA (1965), The Abnormal
Carboxyl Groups of Ribonuclease. II. Positions in the Amino Acid
Sequence, *Biochemsitry*, **4**, 760.

RIEHM, J. P., AND H. A. SCHERAGA (1965), Structural Studies of Ribonuclease.
XVII. A Reactive Carboxyl Group in Ribonuclease, *Biochemistry*, **4**, 772.

SOKOLOVSKY, M., J. F. RIORDAN, AND B. L. VALLEE (1966), Tetranitromethane.
A Reagent for the Nitration of Tyrosyl Residues in Proteins, *Biochemistry*, **5**, 3582.

WOODY, R. W., M. E. FRIEDMAN, AND H. A. SCHERAGA (1966), Structural Studies
of Ribonuclease. XXII. Location of the Third Buried Tyrosyl Residue in
Ribonuclease, *Biochemistry*, **5**, 2034.

INDEX

Abbreviations, of amino acids, 8 ff.
  for peptides, 10
Absorbance in spectrophotometry, defined, 33
Acetic acid, cleavage with, 108, 146
Acid, dilute, cleavage by, 108
  partial hydrolysis by, 107
Acrylonitrile, reaction of, with amino
  groups, 103
  with sulfhydryl groups, 96
Acyl shift, cleavage of polypeptide
  chain by, 110
  at seryl residues, 110
Alanine, abbreviation for, 8
  structure of, 8
Amberlite IR, 18
Amberlite IRA, 18
Amberlite IRC–50, 18
Amidination, modification of tryptic
  action by, 103
Aminoethylation, modification of tryptic action by, 102
β-Aminoethylcysteine, abbreviation for,
  10
  structure of, 10
Amino acid analysis, accuracy of, 58,
  66
  acid hydrolysis before, 64
  automatic, conditions for, 53
    modifications of conditions for, 54
    ninhydrin reagent for, 55
    principles of, 52
  automatic amino acid analyzer for,
    52
  calculation of results of an, 57
  early methods of, 3, 47
  enzymatic hydrolysis before, 66

Amino acid analysis (*Continued*)
  example of an, 56
  factors in separation of components
    in an, 58
  gas chromatographic methods for, 59
  hydrolysis of protein for, 64
  paper methods for, 62
  photometric recording of data in, 55
  preparation of protein for, 64
  quantitative, by ion-exchange chro-
    matography, 51 ff.
  quantitative aspects of, 58, 66
  sensitivity of 57
Amino acid composition, D and L iso-
    mers, 42
  determination of, 47 ff.
    development of methods for, 47
  for estimation of size, 47
  Fischer ester distillation method for,
    3, 47
  Foreman method for, 47
  information from, 41 ff., 47, 136
  Kossel method for, 3, 47
  in maintaining material balance, 47
  means of presenting, 67
  microbiological procedures for, 48
  problems associated with sulfur-con-
    taining amino acids, 43
  significance of relative amounts, 42
  of swine heart fumarase, 59
  uncommon amino acids, 44
Amino acid residue, defined, 7
Amino acid residues, Fischer-Hofmeis-
    ter concept of arrangement of, 3,
    6
Amino acid sequence, abbreviations for,
    10

201

68 69 70   7 6 5 4 3 2 1

207962

DATE DUE

MAY 28 74			
MAY 12 78			
FEB 3 '82			
NO 25 '86			
11/27/13			
GAYLORD			PRINTED IN U.S.A.